Annabel Dover

Florilegia

Moist

First published in 2021 by Moist
https://moistbooks.cargo.site

ISBN ISBN 978-1-913430-04-7
eBook ISBN 978-1-913430-05-4

A catalogue record for this book is available from the British
Library.

Cover design by Annabel Dover with calligraphy by Douglas
Bevans

For Alexei

Preface

Cyanotype is a form of photographic printing process that produces a cyan blue print. Discovered by the English astronomer John Herschel in 1842, cyanotype was initially used to reproduce notes and diagrams later referred to as blueprints. Herschel's friend, Anna Atkins, the daughter of the then famous scientist J.G. Children, soon began to use this technique to record botanical specimens. The result, *Photographs of British Algae: Cyanotype Impressions,* 1843, was the first photographic book ever to be published (preceding Fox Talbot's *Pencil of Nature* by several months).

During her lifetime Atkins produced over 100 uncredited illustrations for her father's translation of *Lamarck's Genera of Shells* (1823) as well as numerous cyanotype albums - some of which were made with the aid of her cousin, Anne Dixon. Her work spawned a cyanotype craze among Victorian women and children. In 1852 Atkins donated these albums, in the form of loose prints, to the Royal Society, the Linnean Society, the British Library, and the Victoria and Albert Museum where they were received as a tribute to her father. They have remained there ever since.

In the introduction to one of her albums, Atkins says that she uses the cyanotype, which 'depicts with the most accuracy possible,' in order to help other botanists. Yet my investigations led me to believe that Atkins doctored and adulterated certain specimens, collaging different sections of different plants together and many of the cyanotypes that she donated may be 'fakes.'

Although Atkins also wrote novels concerned with the fashion and mores of society, and a biography of her father, these writings always sidestep *her* autobiography. There is no official record of Atkins' life beyond that of a dutiful daughter. Yet her albums hold the kernels of a multitude of personal stories that not only tell of her devotion to her parent, but also her love of nature. They reveal much about the attributes thought desirable in a woman of her era: servitude, obedience, and a generous spirit. Many of the institutions to which her albums were donated have since rearranged the loose cyanotype prints, curating and creating their own versions of Atkins' past; a mixture of *naturalis* and *artificialis* with no marked boundaries.

Annabel Dover, 2021

I

The windowless, artificially yellow lit print room on the top floor of the Victoria and Albert Museum is a humidor for disparate collections of paper artefacts; a hospital for fragments. The Museum scooped up the Great Exhibition of 1851 from its original home at the Crystal Palace and ordered it alongside medieval manuscripts written in the January of 1496 when five feet of snow in Genova held people inside. After seeing an elephant on the frozen River Thames George Davis walked home from the last Frost Fair to create the drawings that became *Frostiania: Or a History of the River Thames in a Frozen State*, 1814, recalling the fair of 1536 when King Henry VIII skidded passed in a sleigh on his way to Greenwich, and people ate hot roasted ox. Bear baiting was commonplace just 3.8 miles away from this spot, or a 28 minute tube ride to Bankside, and home to the young Derek Jarman in 1973. Babies died at the rate of one per two births, and the average life expectancy for a person living in Whitechapel was 45 years old.

Figure 1

The Paper Museum, created by Cassiano dal Pozzo and his younger brother Carlo, started as they argued with one another over the classification of nuts. The drawing of a hazelnut tree created by Carlo was later wrongly labelled as an apple tree and credited as anonymous; he painted a face in a hazelnut like a deformed foetus. Cassiano picked the gnarled lemon as the bells of St. Mary Magdalen were hammered and the black carpenter bees cut away at the edges of the leaves he drew. His wife, eight weeks pregnant, was yet to tell him why she was feeling listless and sick.

The hazelnut and malachite drawings are then moved to Buckingham Palace where Hugo Dixon-Smith will die of AIDS in 1986 but say he has cancer. Yet before his illness takes full hold, he still manages to catalogue the Weaponry Collection. Michael Gambon spends his time when not shooting *The Singing Detective* imagining the thrill of a duel at sunrise whilst touching an 18th Century German gun that fires heart shaped bullets.

14 years after the death of her brother-in-law Lucy Dixon-Smith will attend the launch party for the Armoury Collection catalogue at Windsor Castle, and follow the setting sun into the next room to look for the drawings of Cassiano dal Pozzo. She wears grey silk shoes from LK Bennett that cut into her thick ankles, so much so she almost succeeds in getting her stockbroker husband to order a taxi. Instead, she walks her size eight feet over the gravel at Windsor and shreds the 'Midnight Pearl' Dior tights she bought from Dickens & Jones. She had seen a Chelsea Pensioner in the queue, he was buying thermal socks. She joked it must be cold in the barracks and he asked if she was Joanna Lumley. People often did that, especially men over 60. She went out into Sloane Square and saw lumps of ice in the fountain. She remembered the time she worked just two roads away and would go to the Colbert for lunch. One day she saw David Bowie smiling at her through the window, a smile

so full of love and adoration that she said, 'David' back. She went right up to the glass and realised that he was looking at his reflection. She had already touched the window by then and left fuzzy patches of sweat around her fingers, a handprint on the cave wall in Lascaux. She turned around and the waitress said, 'Oh he's done that to me too'.

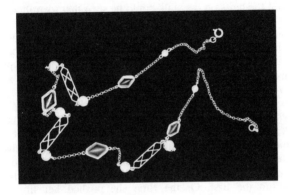

Figure 2

The poppy is like a coffee cup stain, a negative of a plant cut and pressed in 1853 with its thin veined petals. The blue and white print has the night-time glow of a Joseph Cornell ice-cube box or a Stan Brakhage film, the poppy glows candescent but is gone. Anna Atkins' dirty fingernails are pressing the damp skin of the poppy into cotton wadding and blotting paper until the life has dried out of it. The shroud then peels from its body, reveals the sap drenched tears of its stem and days of photosynthesis seeped out and over. She found it on a piece of dry ground, living on grit, with no trace of parent or sibling and perhaps created by a bird who had excreted it. She thinks of the poppy seed buns that her Aunt Emma had made at Easter for her children, and the extra one she always saved for her. Slightly stale, it had journeyed with her in muslin, in a wicker basket that smelled and tasted of her Aunt's King Charles Spaniel, Doublet. Anna could never tell her Aunt about the doggy buns and, as nobody else received food from this basket, she would never know.

The poppy was a sole survivor, Anna picked it when it was vivid and waxy. She had watched it on her way to take letters to the postbox, a small weed at first, and then the hairs on the stalk could be seen that identified it to her as a poppy. The bead of a bud came two days later and divided into a segment. It was at this stage when she was young that she had scored the head open with her jagged thumbnail and seen the crumpled poppy inside, still damp and raw, pale purple and crimped all over. She had felt as if it were humiliating for the plant to be looked at in this stage and akin to how a painter at work feels when watched by an onlooker, as Ruskin had described it . She found it simultaneously irresistible and shameful, like the time she had picked up a mouse the cat had almost killed and folded back its pale pink ear to see another smaller marbled pink ear concealed within the first. Or the time she pushed her fingers inside her father's tortoise Melpo's shell. Melpo had come from Athens and had a frilled skirt like shell that housed an extra bit of flesh and perhaps, she thought, accommodated an organ. Melpo had lived in the Ancient Agora among the hoopoes and magpies, lizards and swallowtails, but now had a restful life in Kent on a striped and glossy lawn, fed with lettuce that hypnotised her into a laudanum haze.

When the poppy flower started to peer out of its green bonnet, Anna came back every half an hour.

The enamel clock in the drawing room makes its sprinkled laughter chime, disturbing the parrot who walks on its mahogany stand away from it, shitting as it goes. A new sound comes from the kitchen. Anna can hear a change of activity often brought on by the chime and guesses that the cook does things in half hour shifts.

The air is warm and dry, and she is glad the poppy wouldn't have its petals knocked off by rain. She touches the most courageous petal and it fastens to her finger like gold leaf. Peeling it off, she grabs its roots and pulls it up. It clings to the ground and some of its roots snap off in vain. Grit stays attached to the specimen in her hand too. The plant and its shadow are gone and there is a small rupture on the ground where it had been.

Hippies in the 1970s went around their gardens warning weeds that they would pull them up the next day, pulling them slightly to ease them into this next phase they claimed the weed gave itself willingly the next day once it knew that its life was over. In the sun she can see the thin, straight hairs on the stem of the plant, like the fine blonde hairs on her upper lip that her husband loves. The poppies Anna picks are not yet associated with World Wars I and II, the first of which will not start for another 62 years and the last will end in 93. It will be nine years until Field Marshal Douglas Haig, 'Master of the Field,' 'Butcher of the Somme' will be born in Charlotte Square, Edinburgh, to the alcoholic millionaire owner of Haig & Haig Whisky Distillers and the great-aunt of Noel Coward. War at this point means fashionable under-bust dresses and the Napoleonic pillboxes of the East Coast that look like castellated jellies. The Californian Indian Wars and the Second Anglo-Burmese War seem remote and the Crimean War won't start until October 1853, in one year's time.

The style of the Empire line dress in the attic lined in dull gold silk and belonging to Anna's mother, is the same as the one worn by Élisabeth Louise Vigée Le Brun at a Greek Supper she hosted in 1788. Smelling of rosewater and the sweat that had eaten away at the pale striped, turquoise watered silk at the armpits, it left obscene proof that her mother had once been alive. Moths had, in a cannibalistic cycle, started to consume the dress. The *Morus Alba* mulberry tree that the moths made the same silk they later ate from still grows. I think of it residing gently in East Timor as I view Anna's blue and white sun print of a poppy which, as I later discover, is called a cyanotype.

Figure 3

The moss that was soft and cooling the first time she bled, the ferns that packaged the delicate china plates in the tea chests when they moved, she drew, using light.

Figure 4

Poppies didn't grow in gardens by accident, unless they were the opium poppy, and then they were only planted by bohemians such as Byron. They flourished in the month of my birthday. The hot sun that forces the ripe belly of the poppy to burst did the same for my mother. After weeks of swollen ankles, and equally pregnant mosquitoes feeding on her blood, she gave birth to me. She bled too much and under anaesthetic talked to the surgeon about gardening, her dislike of hostas and love of hellebores. She came to, and her new husband popped a champagne cork with a sword. The Ward Matron ran in and asked what the sound was and later my mother overheard her say the word 'psychopath'. She thought she would ask her second eldest daughter Esther to get the red Webster's dictionary down from the shelf in the study and look it up, but she forgot.

Figure 5

The night is pale, light silver and Anna Atkins can easily see the poppy petals as she peels them off the blotting paper, parting them with a fuzzy, ripping sound. She removes her husband and her father's books that have pressed the flower down, and places them on the floor where the cat instantly sits, spreading her legs like a gymnast on a pommel horse, washing her furry thighs. She holds the used blotting paper, thinned by the specimen, pressed into a see-through description of a bled out poppy. It is the silhouette of a plant painted in the vegetal juice of its being and the light shines through it like a stained glass window in a dolls' church. The Murano glass ashtray holds the empty cigar ends she tells Sarah the housekeeper to leave. The velvet curtains stink of smoke too. Her husband is in Haiti and she wonders if he'll remember to get the cocoa bean and the chrysalids and whether Lady Ashton will ask her, in that annoying way, if she has missed him. Will he find the Haitian women attractive with their smooth dark skin? She touches the chickenpox dip on her forehead and the mole next to it. It reminds her of a freshly dug grave, a hollow with a mound of earth next to it. She had tried one of her father's cigars when she was on her own in the house once, it had scorched her throat and made her dizzy. It felt like having scarlet fever again.

The largest moon of the year was rising when Elizabeth Barrett Browning picked a cowslip for her *Sonnets from the Portuguese* and pierced the meniscus of water at the mouth of a tiny blue glass bottle with its stalk. The night that Anna was making her poppy cyanotype, the wife of Henry Liddell, the Headmaster of Westminster School, soon to be Dean of Christchurch Oxford, gave birth to Alice, later the inspiration for Lewis Carroll's *Alice in Wonderland*. The midwife had told her that new moons bring about new births.

Disraeli is appointed Chancellor of the Exchequer, the Museum of Manufacturers, predecessor to the Victoria and Albert Museum, is opened at Marlborough House. There is a duel at Priest Hill between two French political exiles: Emmanuel Barthélemy and Frederic Cournet. Cournet is killed. It is the last fatal duel on English soil. Barthélemy, a friend of Victor Hugo, is tried for murder and is instead convicted of manslaughter. Two years later he is hanged for another killing but goes on to be immortalised in *Les Misérables* and as a wax effigy in Madame Tussauds. Anna Atkins writes the name *Papaver Orientale* on the piece of paper that had wrapped the broderie anglaise petticoat she had bought from Denny's in Bishop's Walk. She has already created a comprehensive three volume album of seaweed, and of ferns.

Mathematician and daughter of Byron, Ada Lovelace dies. The first public toilet for women opens as does Great Ormond Street Hospital and the House of Commons, designed by Barry and Pugin. Pugin dies. Thomas Edison draws a quincunx on his forearm with his tattoo pencil machine; maybe his wife Mina's name in Morse code. The cicada grub that John Pelly Atkins brings his wife, Anna, back from Haiti remains underground, buried at the edge of the asparagus patch in their Kent garden for another 17 years. When the cicada finally hatches in 1869 it is surrounded by dahlias. Anna has two years left of her life. Rasputin, Edwin Lutyens, Typhoid Mary, Matisse and Gandhi are born.

French missionary and naturalist Père Armand David is given the skin of a giant panda by a hunter, it is the first time a westerner learns of this species. He also has the 'pocket handkerchief tree,' *Davidia involucrata,* named after him. Meanwhile in France, Hippolyte Mège-Mouriès patents margarine, while elsewhere the Boshin War, the Ten Years War, the Cretan Revolution, the Glorious Revolution and the Red River Rebellion are all stirring.

Figure 6

In 2012, I visited Ormiston, Hadassah Grove, Sefton Park, Liverpool. The owners of the house, a physics lecturer and her husband, a classics lecturer, showed me the Shaker kitchen they had recently put in. Their labrador, Ralph, followed me up the stairs after they warned me to stoop when I got to the attic. They couldn't remember where the light was for the back part. I swiped my hand across the plaster wall until it touched the round Bakelite switch. It fitted exactly in my hand, as satisfying as a soap, and I turned the light on. There, as I leant over the dripping black water tank, were the drawings: a pencil tracing of our cat Isadora, my sister's foot, the profile of 'Leathers' the boy that two of my sisters loved and something I had forgotten about - a piece of my sister's arm cast and on the floor a dried-out piece of yellow Sellotape stuck with short blonde strands of hair from our dog Biscuit.

Tate and Lyle, our guinea pigs, lived and died in this attic and so did the tadpoles that dried up in the Le Creuset pan, leaving the black charcoal patches of their swimming bodies under every casserole I made on top of them at college.

The ruined sofa that used to belong to Ellen Terry rested here too with ha'pennies and Fox Terrier fur wedged into its ripped calico armpits. The picture I drew on the sofa was of a man dropping off a cliff onto some jagged rocks. It was in green felt-tip and I was quite proud of it. Although if I had done it again I might have put a windswept tree on the cliff top. A child psychologist had been called and I was asked to name my friends. I could name six, and I was left alone. The six were my sisters and the cat but the psychologist didn't find that out. I see a mouse lying Ophelia like in a puddle by the back door as I leave.

 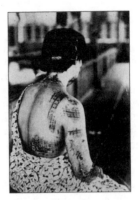

Figures 7 & 8

Sweat draws down the groove of Anna Atkins' back as she lays the dried poppy's body upon dull grey paper. She places the heavy glass once used to frame her nursery sampler onto of the taut dry plant. The sun beats down and makes a rainbow sheen on the glass. The grey paper tarnishes dull copper and Anna picks up the bucket, pushes the glass off with her burgundy kid slippered foot and the water washes the paper flat. The poppy image turns black then a deep poison bottle blue, then white.

Figure 9

The wardrobe that had been in the attic was still there. It was too large and heavy to move from the house and had come straight from Paris to Liverpool with the new owner Professor Zibbert in 1842, the year Anna collected her seaweed samples for her first cyanotype volume. She wonders if she is anaemic as she walks with her friend and cousin Anne Dixon, usually known as Bunny, across the beach at Deal. The pressure of her shoes makes a dainty patch in the gritty sand that is a negative, and then a positive of the pointed slippers that she has quickly squeezed her feet into. The seaweed had to be collected in the water to look like its living self. Wading into the sea with her shoes off and soaking her petticoat, her dress loops around her shoulder and neck like Leda and the swan embracing. She presses the thick rag paper into the water and is amazed at the pressure needed to do so, and then at the strength needed to stop it from being pulled to the bottom. She snaps the seaweed's neck and feels cruel, feels it gasping for air as she does it, before laying it sideways on the paper, spreading its fingers as if it is grasping life in its new death.

The Origin of Painting. July 1778.

Figure 10

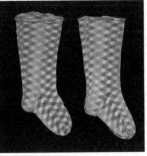

Figures 11 & 12

The wardrobe has ovals of flowers on the two doors that flank the central looking glass. Marquetry garlands cut and stitched together form an elegant, dense pretzel of leaves and flowers and ferns. The glass has turned to mercury and has a pleasing 1970s Vaseline lens reflection with murky silvered silt at the edges; a collection of every reflection it has witnessed. The handprints of past users show up again in a mist of breath.

The sock and scarf drawer housed curled up grubs, after living underground for 20 years they survive for 24 hours or less on the neck or feet and knees of the clothing's owner.

Figure 13

Figure 14

On June 8th, 1871 Anna Atkins raises her sopping wet
arm from the sheet to prop herself up. She had seen that
this was how Rembrandt slept when she visited his
house in Amsterdam and she wonders in her delirium if
she will get to meet him soon. Does heaven have a
chronological order? Are people kept in sections or
areas, eras or geographical countries, class or status?
And would animals be permitted? Sudrowe the cat who
died in childbirth and her mother who died soon after,
would they be angry with her? She looks at the mirror
embedded in the armoire at the foot of the bed. She
knows it is silly, but she hopes that she will become
trapped inside it. She had asked the housekeeper, Sarah,
not to cover it with a black cloth. Sarah believing her to
be foolish and perhaps not superstitious agreed. Anna's
death creeps in early next morning as the rooks make
their sound in the high ash trees at the edge of the
garden and the light turns from blue to white. Sarah and
Aunt Emma pull the key out of the clock in the bedroom
and push the hands to twelve. Emma holds the
pendulum in the long case clock downstairs. Sarah stops
the sprinkling laugh of the Sévres clock in the
Withdrawing Room and then hangs on the weights of
the kitchen clock until it is strangled and stops. The
parrot's cage is covered in mauve felt and the curtains
are drawn. The early June sun presses on the pale cream
cotton linings and gently scorches the lattice of the
windows into their threads.

Figure 15

The huge wardrobe was in the attic when, as young children, my sisters, mother, father and I moved into the house in Liverpool. It had an oval mirror and doors inlaid with garlands of honeysuckle and mother of pearl insects. A few years later it moved with us again, minus my father, to the landing of our new family house in York. It had the words 'Maple & Co Paris' hand painted in gold behind the hangers. Inside the drawers were lots of different socks coiled like fat Danish pastries, thick walking socks with grey flecks, of the kind still sold in old fashioned men's outfitters. These would be our Christmas stockings once a year, holding a deflated satsuma, a piece of coal and some Lakeland pencils. These came from Keswick along with the old fashioned 1960s packet of Kendal Mint Cake that was in the cupboard above the iron. We ate chunks of it when we were desperate. The socks had been my father's mountaineering socks and gone on his feet to Snowdonia and Ben Nevis. His naval coat remained in a plastic shield. My mother talked about a man in uniform and my sisters said it sounded repulsive. The brass buttons had been stripped after his dismissal from the navy. My mother sewed some fake ones on from her Aquascutum wedding coat. Flesh coloured silk ballet shoes lay hidden underneath it. The pocket held an amethyst the size of a scrabble tile that my mother had chosen from a bag of stones from Ceylon, later Sri Lanka.

The other socks belonged to my older brother, Thomas. They were baby socks, pale, an old fashioned ribbed powder blue cashmere worn at the heels by the Startrite shoes he had only just started to walk in. No boy came after. My mother only had girls after that, and I was the last. A case of dead three year-old boy's clothes returned to North London from Uganda, where they'd lived before the tragedy, and now cushioning his bear Edward. The socks curled around themselves. They were the colour of the electric writing at the greyhound track in Romford. They could have warmed the cool marble baby feet that rest on Queen Victoria's writing desk at Osborne House.

Figures 16 & 17

A corner behind the lambskin coat, too dark to look in, held gloves with the initials T.A.M. and F.H.M. sewn inside on Cash's name tapes. My mother's father and son, remnants of their threadbare physical bodies now buried in Uganda and Geneva. In front of these was the damask tablecloth that was used for the family Christmas dinner. Later it ended up being used for the cleaning lady, Mrs Sharpe's, body to be laid out on. I had seen a person laid out before. One of the times I had tried to leave home and walked to Otterspool in the dark. I had stopped to look in the neighbouring Forrestal family's bay window and saw Cis Forrestal, who was in my house at school (Mayflower), lying perfectly still and with the bloom of a frosted plum, on a white cotton sheet, on a table. Her feet were in the white ankle socks she always wore for school, and I wondered why she was wearing them at the weekend. They didn't have the usual grubby footprint that they did during PE. There was nobody else in the room, just their cat Siskin who was curled as tight as a nut on a low nursing chair by the fire. Cis' straggly hair was spread over a pillow, along the table. Hanging over the edge it looked as if it was damp and maybe she had just been swimming. That night, I pulled the old hair out of my boar bristle brush and laid it on my pillow.

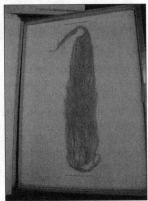

Figures 18 & 19

Next to Thomas' baby socks was a sock belonging to my mother's last husband before my father, Bill: a single sock, washed and sewn with custard coloured wool by the nurses in Essen. It had once rested, curled up by a camp bed with an old LKIM tin. A sock for a foot that no longer existed, his real leg had been lost in the war, then replaced with a cardboard ice-cream cornet made by Russians, then burnt in St. Barth's hospital incinerator along with the matchstick boxes and bookmarks he had once swopped with these same Russians for food.

Figure 20

Wrapped in white tissue paper was a pound of ecclesiastical silk, and a scarf belonging to my mother's first husband, Francis. It had been woven by hands who had witnessed women with bound feet but not the Cultural Revolution, shipped to Liverpool, taken to Silver Stree, Cambridge in an enamelled green Austin van and displayed in Ede & Ravenscroft's Gentleman's Outfitters. The ivory knitted scarf is stained with something yellow that looks like rust; a brass key that was wrapped in it left an indelible mark. 'Trinity Hall' is written in small self-conscious copperplate on the label, the same two words that adorn the flyleaf of Francis' copy of *Paradise Lost*, shortly followed by his other notes. These were an anagram of notes written at Trinity Hall by J. B. Priestly. Priestly had lived in Francis' room previously, and also written about the symbolism of Satan, struggled with hangovers and left the burgundy linen curtains semi-drawn as the rain ran down the leaded windows and his vision of the quad was reduced to a misty green lozenge. Priestly had looked at the cracks in the ceiling and seen them as donkey's ears, just as Francis did 33 years later.

Nestled inside the Trinity Hall scarf like the stamen of a fat silken flower was my mother's Guerlain Mitsouko soaked headscarf embroidered with angry geese. We, her children, were allowed to wrap the goose scarf around our necks when we had a sore throat.

My mother's 34C bras were kept here too, before her breasts turned, after five children, to loose stockings. Her tulle nightgown and bed-jacket, reminders of her pre-baby sex life, that my sisters and I wore as evening dresses to our fantasy debutante balls. I didn't understand the point of the nightgown being see-through. Period stained sheets from five different wombs also arrived here to make patchy ghosts and to be ripped up to polish the silver.

Figure 21

The jet buttons on the astrakhan cape have been rubbed. The unborn calf, still crinkled, pulled out of its mother's womb to make the glossy ringlet fur that once shimmered in sunlight. A button could be rubbed to counteract bad luck if a funeral procession was encountered and there was no escape. Anna Atkins starts to turn around as she abruptly meets the procession of the funeral for the Starkey's boy. She pushes her thumbnail into the tartan pattern of the cut jet button and continues walking instead. She had felt hurt by seeing the Alderton girl turn around at the sight of her father's funeral.

It is August 1853 and Josephine Boisdechêne, recently married to Fortune Clofullia, starts performing as the Bearded Lady for Mr. Barnum's Museum of America. Charles Darwin receives the queen's medal at the Royal Society for his work as a scientist and the world's first aquarium opens at London Zoo. In the kitchen Aunt Emma uses the horsetails that Anna has cut with a carving knife from the corner by the potato patch. She guts them and then wraps their prehistoric bodies in a dishcloth and scrubs John's silver tray with their silica oozing stems.

Figures 22 & 23

In the glass compartment of my mother's wardrobe named handkerchiefs, there was a round, red and gold leather box of collars and studs that I never understood, a packet of ancient condoms, a copy of *How to Win Friends and Influence People,* and Len Deighton's *Twinkle Twinkle Little Spy.*

Figure 24

John Pelly Atkins no longer took precautions. Anna had never become pregnant and he guessed it was God's wish that at 41 she would never be a mother. He felt guilty at the wet patch she left on the sheets and mattress each month and the sodden moss she dried and burnt in the grate curled up to smoky nothingness.

Figure 25

On top of the wardrobe, out of sight, rested my uncle's rigid Freemason case. It held a slab of material woven with thread that persistently bullied a thin cotton square, the cardboard enforced moiré silk, and the Egyptian eye that I would see much later in the stained glass window of a lodge, folded neatly into a 1950s housewife style apron. There were white gloves too, of the kind I would wear later when I cleaned the glass cabinets of fish shaped silver perfume bottles in the National Trust property I worked for, Ickworth House. Leaning over the mirrored table, smearing off the Christmas Cactus juice drops, I could always see the scars on my chin. Sometimes, as I arrived in the room at 7am, I could smell cigar smoke coming through the keyhole of the Billiard Room. The Marquis still lived in the east wing. I could hear the crack of billiard balls hitting one another, quiet laughter and the chink of cut glass tumblers being toasted. Once I looked in and saw three young boys lying asleep on the floor, like labrador puppies in a basket

Figure 26

The paper curls up like a fortune teller fish in the hand. The ghost of a poppy is left, and its spirit transferred to the paper forever. Anna places it in a rice paper shroud and blots it dry under her father's *Atlas of the Empire* and *The Mode in Costume*.

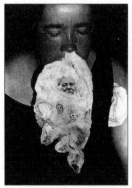

Figures 27 & 28

My sister Susannah had a pair of ersatz Levi's with one back pocket and a deep indigo patch where the other pocket had come off. She wore them with white plimsolls and a light blue sweatshirt, printed with dark blue writing, from an Outward Bound holiday in Matlock. From the moment they arrived from the charity shop, the jeans were never washed. My mother complained of the dirt they left on her side of the double bed. A filthy palimpsest lay next to my father even when Susannah had gone, and he lay asleep all morning and all afternoon. The shadow within a shadow left an impression in my mind. I recently saw it again: a dark patch where there had been a pocket. I saw my sister in those jeans so often I saw them as her skin, the darker blue was the inside of her body, bleeding out like an uncapped felt-tip and the grubby leg shaped marks that seeped into my mother and father's sheets seemed to me, to be her skin rubbing off.

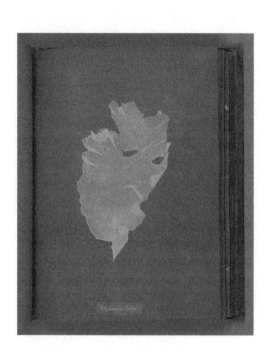

II

In 1786, the last wolf in Ireland is killed in Myshall, County Carlow by a pack of Irish wolfhounds. 13 years later the dogs are all dead, Anna Atkins is born, and two days after that her mother dies. In 1861 Anna Atkins, in her 60s, and her cousin Anne, or Bunny, make a final album for their young, blonde nephew, Captain Henry Dixon.

Figure 29

Prince Albert's face greys as quickly as a beach covered by a cloud and he closes his eyes. The wife of the choirmaster of St Paul's is woken by the doleful tolling of the bell at 10.20 at night. The Prince's name is omitted from the prayers for the royal family the next day. Queen Victoria continues to have his wash basin filled, and his filigree silver pocket watch from Cologne wound every night until she dies 40 years later. Queen Victoria and later Freud ask their staff to make an inventory of their belongings. Freud has his maid reposition his objects in the same arrangement as they were in Vienna once he arrives in Hampstead. Queen

Victoria has her objects photographed from every angle, and these photographs are put into albums for her to look at. So enormous is her collection, she can only view it in miniature.

Dante Gabriel Rossetti draws the painter Joanna Boyce with a silverpoint as she dies after giving birth to a fat baby girl, Joanna Margaret Boyce. A heart shaped tin holding what is rumoured to be Ann Boleyn's heart is discovered during renovations on the chancel of St. Mary's church in Yorkshire, and on June 29th Elizabeth Barrett Browning wakes to hear the swifts outside her window. Her milk came in last night and her breasts are cow heavy. The Florentine sun casts a loom across her cheeks and illuminates her green-grey eyes. She is wet with hot sweat and her husband holds her as she dies.

Figure 30

It is a hot day in Tonbridge too, and Anna Atkins is unaware for another week that Elizabeth Barrett Browning is dead. The miasma kills hundreds of people on a day like today in London. Anne presses the bell at 10.30 in the morning. The maid hasn't wound the doorbell up completely and it quavers like a sick choirboy.

Anna watches as Bunny slowly bends her head down into the coats and hats that hang in the porch, her skirts rustling. Her lips touch General Carruthers' velvet skull. He sits on a corduroy covered chair, hidden under Anna's Sunday jacket. Like a muffler in a roly-poly pudding position his paws are tucked in and he closes his eyes in contentment. The cat kissing ritual is medieval, or so Bunny has told Anna. Bunny was very much taken with Darwin's *The Expression of Emotion in Man and Animals* and she was upset when she finally met the great Charles, as Anna's father called him, at dinner. She waited until the mutton had been served and leant gently across to tell him about her love of animals. He seemed irritated and scratched his beard. On Bunny and Anna's walks together, Bunny would help animals; last week for example, she moved a toad to some mud under a protective hellebore and it oozed acid on her hand as it struggled to escape.

They go through their finds for the sun prints:

> String from the New Year's Day goose
> Ostrich feathers
> Pheasant feathers found in the woods, killed by the dog
> fox that sometimes comes into the garden
> Pencil shavings
> Lace from Seraphina Rowe's worn out petticoat
> Feathers from the pillow
> Sargent's fur (Springer Spaniel)
> Flowers from Thomasina's funeral
> A butterfly that got trapped in the study in the hot
> August sun
> A dandelion seed, head mostly intact
> Fingernail clippings (Bunny says no to these)
> Lace gloves
> Part of the broken Chinese parasol
> Talcum powder
> A spider
> Hair from the brush
> A broken cut glass necklace
> Net from Emilia's bonnet
> A handkerchief
> Water lily leaves from the pond that have skeletonised
> A cucumber slice, pressed

Anna tells Anne that their cook, Margaret, received Mrs. Isabella Beeton's book last week and the recipe for fried cucumber was quite disgusting. Isabella Beeton loathes cooking. She prefers fashion and becomes fashion editor for *The Queen* magazine. Four years later at the age of 28 she dies after a series of miscarriages resulting from syphilis; her husband likes to visit prostitutes in Burlington Arcade. There is a report in the newspaper that the MacAllistair sisters are asphyxiated by night-time flowers after their nanny forgets to remove a vase of Cornish violets from their room before bedtime.

Anne tells Anna that she has read a poem by a female slave. She is reading Admiral Nelson's letters now, and he calls his wife's *mons veneris*, his 'little thatched cottage'. Anne opens the door to the garden holding the chemical soaked paper. She looks up to see the ghost moon above the yew. René Lalique's mother makes a final exhausted push whilst closing her eyes and her baby is born, as purple and squashed as the dead pigeon chick Anna found on the lawn last week.

Figure 31

A hundred years later, the gloam of a glass woman rides past the lucky cat and the Coca-Cola neon on Piccadilly Circus. Her opalescent breasts glow lilac, her knees are bent as if wading into a river, her close cropped bob is sleek in the wind and the flats of her arms are raised to the midnight sky. Kenneth Clarke's Rolls Royce *Silver Wraith* glides by Eros on its way from The Ritz to his castle.

Figure 32

I tread on a tiny nugget of glass in Père Lachaise cemetery. Wilde's huge sailboat of a tomb covered in lipstick kisses, docks close to the wall where the communards were shot and where Delacroix and thoughts of his maid lie rotting. Autumn leaves cover a shard of broken bottle. I try to pick it up. It is a clod of amber glass and marks the remains of René Lalique.

Figure 33

In 1894 Coca-Cola is served in bottles for the first time, a syzygy of planets occurs when Mercury transits the sun, The Owl Club of Cape Town has its first formal meeting, Alfred Kinsey of the Kinsey Report is born along with Jean Renoir, and Henry James stays in the Hotel Palazzo Abadessa, overlooking the lagoon in Venice.

Figures 34 & 35

Mr Henry James esquire, author of 'the two most brilliant novels in the English language' sees that she, Constance Fenimore Woolson, had rearranged the objects on the desk, and he ignored it. Two of his cigar stubs were lined up like warships docking at Portsmouth Harbour next to what looked like the lump of sugar he gave her at the Hotel Danieli as a joke. The thick, crocheted lace at the window left a mosaic shadow of a little girl holding a basket on the marble floor. The roses were much earlier in Venice than in New York City, they pulsated and curled towards him, raspberry ripple streaks on veined petals. A stargazer lily stamen, laden with sweet pollen drops its cocoa powder dust on the marquetry. He can feel them inhaling his breath and gaining vitality.

He had 'mm'd' as Constance showed him her album: other peoples' photographs of the Doge's Palace and then the one of her brother Phillip standing in the water, his feet magnified. He had felt irked by this image, it seemed an obscene photograph and he had told her so. She had laughed. 'Phillip is only a boy.' But Phillip's strong brown ankles infected him like a fever. At night when he couldn't sleep, and despite the rising spring heat he had put his worsted socks on to cover his own pale feet.

Henry regarded the flushed dome that she resided in both day and night. The rosary on a nail above the occasional table, the plush pile on the heavy curtains. How many other peoples' breath had they absorbed? An engraving of a gerbil standing on its hind legs, where had that come from? The brocade on the cushions looked like it should be on an altar. She was quiet now and he saw that her eyes had the sheen of fresh raindrops. He saw the glittering drops at her ears, the ash in the grate from the night before. 'A perfect Voltaire in petticoats' is what he had called their hostess Clover Adams. 'Which writer am I?' Constance had asked him, and he couldn't think.

As Henry looked at Phillip's paisley scarf on the back of a chair he noticed that his tongue flattened to the roof of his mouth in the way that he had he felt his spirit rise to the roof of Chartres Cathedral on beholding it for the first time. The King Charles spaniel stretched the large eyes under her ginger eyebrows momentarily up towards him and then closed them again. A squadron of swifts squealed at the window baring their breasts, and he imagined how painful it must be to never land on the ground, sleeping, mating and eating on the wing as they did for years.

He kissed Constance goodbye. She smelled of icing sugar, of dust, and of Lily of the Valley; how he imagined a female moth might smell. A faintly metallic odour too arose from her noisy skirts and he stepped back onto the edge of the rug and felt the uncomfortable lump of a silk tassel under his leather sole. He perceived her pale cheek bloom under his lips, and thought of the repulsive shock he had felt, on instruction from his nanny, to touch the central spine of a mimosa leaf and watch as it curled to forefinger. 'Isn't that wonderful Henry?' nanny had said, 'That's why it's called the sensitive plant'. Later she asked him why he no longer used the sponge in the bath once she had told him it was an animal. The dog groaned and he thought how the brown patches under her eyes made her look as if she'd been crying. She had her paws out in front now like the Landseer lions in Trafalgar Square. He knew he should ask for his umbrella. Constance's friend Justine stood up behind him 'What a fine, jolly buttonhole Mr James' she said looking at his lapel and opened her palm towards the door. Behind her was a frail pile of skeleton leaves and other feminal fandangles that were ordered with what seemed to him the taxonomy of a lunatic. He was suspicious of anything Justine said after he overheard her remark that he reminded her of a satyr. He had taken care to keep his side whiskers in meticulous order since then and they were never again allowed to cross the boundary line demarcated by his mole.

It had been the next evening whilst closing his eyes and listening to the gentle fizz of the lump of ice swell and butt the cut glass of his Perrier, that Henry had learned Constance was dead. She had jumped from her window, broken her neck.

The lagoon was foul and smelled of hundreds of years of Venetian dinners rotting at the base of the wooden stumps that held it up. There is sea smoke above it like a low thundercloud and the women had pulled their starched laundry in. Holding a plump bundle of her dresses, Henry asked the young gondolier to take him to the deepest part of the lagoon, 'Acqua piu profonda,' he had said in an offhand way. 'Si Signor James' the gondolier said quickly.

The boathook slung down the side of the gondola looked like the one that his friend Arlo had used to open the windows of the schoolroom. The brass of the hook was polished beautifully, the boy's nails he had noticed were clean, bar the white spots of malnutrition and he felt glad that he has chosen this gondolier: clean and inexperienced. Sitting down in the boat, he looked at the colour of the fabric in his hands which he knows to be puce. Once he had picked a still warm sandy hare up by its long silken ears and seen a spray of animalcules jump onto his bare forearm. Grabbing one between his fingers and thumb he saw its blood filled body wriggling against the trammels of his fingerprint and let it go. It jumped onto his neck. Later he saw a speckled blood stain on his collar.

Figures 36

The gondolier looked across the lagoon and Henry threw the dresses overboard. He saw them float on the surface. They pulsated like a cloud of jellyfish and clung to the side of the boat. The dresses inflated, the plum coloured silk grows into breasts and the full skirt became buoyant. He pushed them down into the water with the pole and they bobbed up elsewhere. The loose smocked waist filled and ripened like the furry fruit on his Grandfather's schumacher tree, the fruit he had used to push into water to make pink 'lemonade.' Standing up he pressed the wet crinoline as deeply as he could and lurched in the boat. He held the bodice down and it swelled up in a rush. A wet purple bulge like a cow's bladder inflated and engulfed the end of the boathook and pulled his stomach towards it. He felt that the boat might overset, and he broke the pole free and rested it, dripping, on the red velvet seat of the gondola. The droplets pooled and were then absorbed leaving dark patches.

The gondolier looked up at the driver of the passing water taxi, Paulo. Instead of his familiar 'Ciao!' the gondolier remained mute and looked into his friend's eyes for as long as he could. He touched his own cheek with one hand before replacing it behind his back in the stance of an English tourist in a museum. Henry saw a glint of her hair flash gold in the reflection of light on the water, it is wound tightly around a bone button. Another button, this one jet, floated up and he almost grabbed it. His stomach tightened as he realised he had left the lapis brooch on the bodice of the dress, the one she was wearing in Boston, the first time they met. It held his gaze as it sank slowly towards the carpet clams. Constance's final dress had a cotton undergarment concealed within it. It crawls out of the skirts in the water and spread its paper white arms to the sky.

Later, in his room, as he lay his dress shirt on the bed, Henry saw the Rorschach sweat patches on the cotton, and wondered if the Shroud of Turin would be worth seeing.

The oily scum on the lido puddles into marbled patterns.

Afterwards, Constance's chin looked like it had been badly carved out of butter. Her eyelashes were long and blonde. She was wearing white cotton which she had never done in life. She had a bruise under her eye and what looked like pastry moulded to her cheekbone, it was the same colour as the skin on her face but a different texture and for the first time Henry wanted to touch her. He saw the watercolour veins of her hands. He'd never seen her so close. Her nails were perfect, buffed but matt like sugared almonds. He saw a sliver of a gap between her lips and could just about decipher what looked like Gamgee tissue. A woman came to kiss her body. She whispered to it in Latin. As she moved the knot of hair resting on Constance's throat, he was shocked to see a piece of wire had been pushed through the neck of the body and into the lilac satin pillow below. He did not attend the funeral.

Once she had gone, he began to love her.

The silk and cotton rotted on the lagoon bed, carpet clams made their homes in them and were served to Mariano Fortuny, in a vongole, as he dined at the Osteria al Cantinon. Later, Henry James' writing was described as being that of a man who 'watches life from a window, rather than participating.'

*

It is ten in the morning and the peppered moth rests on the corrugated bark of a willow tree in the village of Bollington. It is 1870 and the female infanticide act has just been passed in India, African American men have just been given the right to vote, Old Faithful geyser in Yellowstone is observed and named, Charles Darwin dies and Maria Montessori is born. Ellen Shearing hears the sound of water on the flat slates in the stream outside, which makes her need a piss most of the time. She heard the cotton fluff they fed into the machine came from a hot country, she knew that the Lamb of Tartary wasn't true, there wasn't a spring sheep babe with a blue silk ribbon around its woolly neck growing from a plant in India. She unbuttons the top of her chemise and lifts her sore breast into the hole in the door. There is a cold breeze on her nipple, and she imagines what it must look like on the other side to see a blue veined globe in a circle of wood, like the holes in the boards with a strongman and a mermaid painted on at the South Pier in Blackpool. How did sailors do the things they wanted to do to Mermaids?

Ellen feels a hot tug on her nipple and hopes it is her baby girl. A nursemaid chides the baby on the other side 'Stop wriggling now, you naughty boy'. She looks at the grain of the wood that is close to her face and wonders how old the tree is, when it was cut down, and why it looks like the whorl on her fingertips. Lewis had told her that you can find out how old a whale is by its ear wax. The baby finishes, Ellen lets go of the door and sees she has a splinter in her thumb. It runs like a purple shard under the nail. The pain makes her gasp as she lifts her breast back into her cotton top. When she gets back to the jenny she feels she might cry. She doesn't choose Lizzy, who is kindly and sweet, but Sarah, the poison pudding to remove the splinter. Sarah comes towards her with a pair of nail scissors and a bodkin. Her breath smells of tobacco, the clay pipe that lay cracked on the wall outside must be hers. Ellen had watched the rain empty it. Silently, Sarah cuts the nail until it is thinly covered with papery skin. Years afterwards, at Sarah's funeral, her husband will say he only ever saw her with a sour expression, and that she scowled in her sleep. But after she pulls the snag of oak from Ellen's thumb, Sarah looks into Ellen's eyes and curls the edge of her mouth upwards like a nursery rhyme cat.

*

In Tamil Nadu which, under British colonial rule, is now part of the Madras Presidency, Pari rests her head on the unsorted cotton. It will soon be shipped to England, and after many hot, airless weeks in the cargo hold it will eventually be unloaded in Bollington. Pari lies with her body sideways on the cool floor. The ortolan bunting have been stealing the sticky seed coat made from human hair, jute, metal, dust and grass that are whipped up in the lint. She feels a dismal ache like a metal pan in the stomach. All she can think about is the seersucker she wore meaning sugar and milk: the smooth of the milk stripe and the jagged crystal lumps of sugar for the yellow stripe. She had hidden two things in the hole in the drumstick tree this morning. She sees the ortolan rise from its earthly nest to sing at heaven's gate, its smooth body so small it could rest in her cupped hand.

*

'Today you will learn to eat ortolans' Aunt Alicia says to Gigi in Collette's novella.

*

The Parisian dinner guests place large, white linen napkins on their heads to savour the smell, and then eat each bird whole, all bones intact, like a car in a crusher. The guests spit the bones out under the napkins, and then remain under them hiding from the eyes of God. The dinner resembles an eyeless assembly of the Ku Klux Klan. Roman Emperors stabbed the birds' eyes out to make them think it was night so that they would gorge themselves on millet. They grew like a veal calf or white asparagus, disorientated and delicious in the dark. Drowned in a vat of armagnac these ortolans are served illegally. On New Year's Eve in 1995 President Mitterrand eats 30 marennes oysters, a capon, a quarter of a pound of foie gras, and two ortolans, and 8 days later dies from prostate cancer. Each bite starts to taste of his own blood as the bones prick his mouth, figs, fat, meat and organs. He dribbles as he feels the beak and the ortolan's tongue with his tongue and the cropped feathers on the skull. He crushes it between his back teeth.

Figures 37 and 38

My grandparents spoke loudly to one another between the bedroom and the bathroom opposite. I saw them from the landing at night. Their pubic hair had fallen out. Once, Timmy the Siamese must have pushed the door open to their bedroom. My grandmother was asleep on her back, her Marks and Spencer nightdress with the autumn leaf pattern was worn and showed the slump of her low-slung bosoms slipping down under her armpits. Next to her Margaret Priseman from church was asleep with her head on my grandfather's chest. Romeo, the standard poodle, was lying at the foot of the bed. His glossy marble eyes looked at me. Timmy 'waaahed' like a crying baby. I was too frightened to go to the loo, so I went back to bed, peeing on a puddle of Earl Grey in my mother's teacup instead.

*

The walls of the upper floor flat in 25 Noel Road, Islington have a vast population of onlookers pasted onto them: Henry the VIII, Donatello's shepherd boy, Saskia Rembrandt, the Virgin's head cast down in shame, the naked Maya, the three Magi, the Lady with an Ermine, Bacchus looking queasy.

Dr J. D. K. Burton, the deputy coroner for St Pancras, adjourned the inquest after only three minutes as the doctor called to give evidence was on holiday in Cornwall. John Kingsley Orton was identified by his brother Mr Douglas William Orton, of Ambleside Drive, Leicester. Mr Orton, a plumber, was a slight man dressed in a dark blue suit and light blue shirt. He stepped down from the witness box after only a few seconds. Mrs S. Pearl, Mr John Orton's daily, identified Mr Halliwell also leaving the box within seconds. The coroner then ordered the adjournment and apologised for starting the case fifteen minutes late. Mrs Pearl's statement to police follows:

"I was Mister Joe Orton and Mr Kenneth Halliwell's cleaner there from 1964 to 1967. I came in once a week and did whatever was asked of me.

Whenever I looked at Kenneth, I saw his big round back. He reminded me of a hedgehog, much more back than front, and more like Mrs Tiggwinkle than Fuzzypeg. Joe walked around the flat naked like a man on one of those Greek urns, he was so cheeky. He loved looking at his silhouette on the wall and called it 'the shadow of Mr Punch'. And sometimes he left me things on the table when he was making his collages: a cat because he knew I liked cats, that had been cut into the shape of a cock. He told me quite a few things. Once when he was lying in bed with asthma he found out it was my birthday. He told me Lady Day, 25th March, was the start of the New Year in the old days.

'Just in time for Spring cleaning eh?' and then 'Fark off,' imitating me before I had actually said it. Some people I cleaned for thought I enjoyed it. My mother laughed, 'You a cleaner! My days.' I said 'That's right' but thought of Joe saying 'Fark off' in my head. He gave me some chocolate on my birthday. He had stolen loads when they worked at Cadbury's and they kept it all in the bathroom cabinet, next to the rolled-up snake of a posh school tie Kenneth had got from somewhere. He'd never even been to the school.

When I asked him 'Do you want a cream cake with your tea?' he'd answer by mouthing 'Are they homosexuals?' impersonating his mother, like 'Is the Pope a Catholic?' It's what she always said around Joe's friends. I'd always say, 'Stop it Joe,' but sometimes I'd ask him stupid questions just to make him do it because it made us laugh so much.

The little hedgehog took 22 of his Nembutal pills and drank them down with the juice from the tin of canned grapefruit I'd left on the side for Joe. Joe's sheets were still warm when they found him. They said his head was cratered like a burnt candle."

*

In 1983 Klaus Barbie is arrested in Bolivia, wearing a seatbelt becomes mandatory in the UK, and Michael Jackson performs the Moonwalk for the first time. 'Hitler's Diaries' are published and later discovered to be forgeries.

Figure 39

'Haven't seen one of those ties for quite some time,' says the consultant to my father.

My father does a loud echoing laugh. I knew he'd wear Francis' tie today.

'Do you know Bob Osborne-Hays?' says the consultant.

'Bobby! Know and love him' says my father.

'Hahahaha are you a member of the squash club?'

'Hate to say it. Spend most of my life there!'

'Good man. Good man.'

I try looking in the eyes of the student doctor. He looks away.

'Nothing to worry about here.'

'It miiight be an allergic reaction I suppose. Just a hygiene issue I imagine.'

'Yes, oh dear, she's a mucky Arab.'

'You're a doctor?'

'No no,' says my father, like he'd dismissed the idea as a weak choice. 'Run a children's home. For my sins.'

'Tough work. Rewarding I imagine.'

'Seen the E-type in the car park?' continues my father

'What a beauty.'

'My father-in-law has one, never lets me touch it though.'

'Who can blame him?'

Guffaws and handshakes. I look one last time at the student doctor, but he has his head bowed. The nurse ignores me. I see my father has pressed my mother's Max Factor Creme Puff in Gay Whisper over his Borstal quincunx tattoo. The blue dots show through the powder: the prisoner inside the four walls.

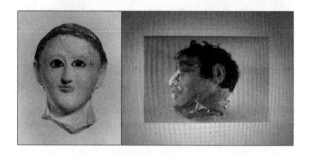

Figures 40 & 41

Stanley Eavis was my grandfather. He was proud of his E-type Jaguar. He came from a poor family that did something unglamorous and poorly paid to do with grain. He was clever in a boring way and patented some things to do with lightbulbs. He owned 13 factories and had a chauffeur and later a plane. When I knew him, he wore big rust coloured cotton trousers that looked like Thames barge sails on his thin legs. He had a huge nose and ears both of which my mother inherited. His voice sounded like the foghorn at Alcatraz and he liked talking about money. '50 K' he would say, looking at the FT, smirk and pat his Siamese cat Timmy hard on the arse. He would get very angry if he didn't eat on time, sometimes fainting as my grandmother, Mikey, was talking about chicken stock not being quite ready. Mikey didn't know anything about chicken stock as she never cooked, that was left to the woman who helped her, Pat. Pat got a huge love bite when, the weekend before her daughter's wedding, a hot fish finger fell off the high grill onto her neck. She always looked as though she was imagining her way out of her present situation. It's a look I've seen on life models' faces since and one I always had in PE lessons. 'You are never in your own body' Miss Lister had told me, like it was a bad thing.

Figure 42

It was not surprising when Mikey's heavy gold charm bracelet with the names of grandchildren, children, and cousins went missing and was then melted down. I hated that bracelet because I had a different script from everyone else, tackier and more ornate, and my brother, Thomas' disc was placed the other way around because he was dead. It reminded me of the suicide grave in the churchyard. I also hated it because it looked like a chain link fence. I was glad Pat stole it along with a large rainbow opal with chips of refracted sunlight, reined in by a tight gold band: an electric jelly.

Stanley was Churchwarden and once he got a priest to exorcise the boot of his Volkswagen Passat because it had contained candles and tree branches that people practicing black magic had left behind the altar. We weren't allowed to call a Stanley Knife a Stanley Knife in front of him. He went doolally in the end and stopped speaking with an R.P. accent, returning to his Leicester twang. After he died, I found lots of ham radio stuff, an old Christmas Radio Times, the minutes from diocese meetings, RSPB subscriptions and a scrapbook in the heavy oak drawers stamped with 'Heal's'.

My grandmother Mikey had given me a scrapbook like this. It had a picture of Holly Hobby on it and she bought it for me the same time she bought me Panda Pops and a Wildlife bar. She didn't accept her pension, she said that was for poor people. The post office shop was in a caravan in a field and had warning posters about rabies and Colorado beetles. I was so disappointed when I found out the Colorado beetle I had caught was a ladybird nymph.

I was excited when I opened my grandfather's scrapbook and saw a collage of a mottled pink octopus. Then I looked at its hairy mouth and realised it was a woman. Like Ingres he'd taken different parts of different women and collaged them together into raw chimeras. One looked like Helen, the postman's daughter. She'd been born with her feet on back to front. There was a black woman's glossy slender thighs and an Asian woman's face, marshmallow pink breasts with Turkish delight nipples. Some of the faces were composed of different parts too, like Henry Tonks' Guinea Pig Club: Linda Grey's sapphire eyes (this shocked me, we would never have been allowed to watch *Dallas*) with Mariel Hemmingway's catlike wide cheeks, and from a photograph my sister had taken, my mouth. He had coloured in the gaps with my Mothercare clean easy felt-tips and the pen had seeped into the sugar paper making the women look like they'd been flayed: Simon Weston faces flashed on Hannah Hoch bodies.

Figures 43

Coming out of the loo in the Rose & Crown on Lower Sloane Street I felt a tug and thought I must have my hair caught on a chair. I turned around and saw a Chelsea pensioner holding it in his hand. He recited a poem about his Danish daughter, Amelia, and her aquatic life in the womb. Her described her eyes as Whitby jet. He hated the X-Factor but most of all Carol Thatcher, he loathed vulgarity and respected Rodin's *The Kiss*. This he thought was something beautiful, love not lust. He thought of his Danish wife and daughter and felt they had been washed away on an ice flow in the night.

After seeing Alan Clarke combing his hair in the reflection of the window of his Navy Jaguar XJS parked outside Albany Mews, I walked to the Royal Academy and then put my arms through my holey fairisle cardigan whilst waiting for the life drawing students to come in. Lying down naked on the sofa I looked at the plaster cast of Stubbs' horse and the flayed smuggler and fell asleep.

 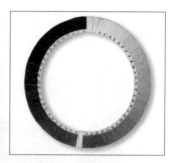

Figures 43 & 44

Lady Hertford, later known as the Prince of Wales' mistress, takes the recently published John James Audubon's *Famous Birds of America* and begins to cut a flamingo from its page. Later in her bedroom at Temple Newsam she tries to get warm and writes to her sister:

> *The weather is beastly cold and grey as usual and I really find Yorkshire to be a most miserable place. Visitors tell me that it is so verdant and lush but really my view of the arboretum might be lovely if it were not constantly smeared with rain. Even squinting with one eye at Peterson's folly this morning allowed only for the impression of an indecipherable ink blot through the windowpane. Juliette is well, her favourite new habit is not one I hope she exhibits in public. She searches for grit in her hair with her little fingers and on finding some eats it in the hope that it is sugar from a bun she had at teatime. She seems almost as pleased when she discovers it is soil from the gardens.*
>
> *I do not know about George. It is all exciting but, Edward is as you might imagine seething,*

and my confiscation to Ireland rather inflamed him. He is determined I become his paramour. He sent me huge reams of paper for the walls of the Chinese Dining Room and I lavished it upon them. The house drank them up like a cat in the sun, how in need it is of cheer and exoticism.

Later she writes again:

He does suffer as his father did and his corpulence now precludes him from mounting the stairs let alone the pleasures we once shared. I found the book that Edward gave me. Such a vast book and such beautiful plates that I knew it would enliven the tropical walls of the dining room. I carefully cut each bird from its page and with hoof glue and a sable brush pressed them into place in their new fantastic home. The room looks alive with creatures and I can almost hear their musical cries. I am so excited for George to visit and for him to see what I have done!

George III mistakes a large tree for a Prussian King and his son becomes Regent. He has the Brighton Pavilion built and dips his gouty feet into the sea. During the First World War the Pavilion was again used for recuperation and served as a military hospital for the Indian Corps; gaining consciousness they beheld a phantasm of India. George's surgeon was at a loss. Piss is not generally purple, true, but his father had the same and perhaps George's royal blood made him prey to afflictions mortals could never suffer. His supply of laudanum could barely satisfy the King's ravenous demand and the corset that they made for him at Ede & Ravenscroft could no longer hold his waist to 50 inches. Near 20 stone he'd puffed up and each of his limbs too. His braces looked like the string on the Sunday lamb and a normal chair could not cradle his buttocks. He was breathless to near asphyxiation and when naked he looked as though he were a sausage stuffed into its covering. At half past three on the morning of 26th June, 1830, at Windsor Castle, he yelled to his page, 'Good God, what is this?' grabbed his hand and said, 'My boy, this is death.' A tumour the size of one of Sloane's oranges clung to his bladder. His stomach, a mound of blood, and his heart was as waxen as a 12th Night stilton.

Lady Hertford arranges for an avenue of trees to be planted in a quincunx formation to commemorate him: four beeches protecting one pine, like five dots on a die. The nightjars nestle their downy underparts onto the rustling copper leaves and warm their eggs under the third quincunx. Meanwhile Napoleonic sailors arriving in Southwold cut drawings of anchors and women into the trunks of the beech and pine trees there, and by the 1900s the trees are called the Butley Clumps.

The Audubon collage on the walls of Temple Newsam remains protected from the light with blinds. The trestle tables are set up on the lawns of the house. It is 1922 and under a cedar tree the glittering silver lies on a trestle table. The New Year frost casts a crisp, sugary layer on the grass and the objects laid out for the sale look like maidens in bud. The British Empire rules over one in four people in the world. Christian K. Nelson has just patented the Eskimo Pie, and Samuel Gravely, who will become the first African American fleet commander is born in Richmond, Virginia. Shackleton, Proust, the Barbary lion, and the Californian grizzly bear all become extinct. Proust is buried in Père Lachaise cemetery in a double bed sized grave with his sports loving brother and both parents. Judy Garland is also born. At the close of the year Virginia Woolf's *Jacob's Room* is published and Howard Carter and Lord Carnarvon enter the tomb of Pharaoh Tutankhamun, the first people to do so in over 3000 years. 88 years later the crates of whiskey that were buried beneath Shackleton's Antarctic hut are discovered and tasted.

Figure 46

Dorothy Wood is the final inhabitant of Temple Newsam, prior to its being sold. As she walks out of the garden room and onto the lawn she remembers her baby fingernails under the floorboard in the nursery. The coil of her red hair before it turned pale yellow and then white in the corner under the bath. The comb that fell through the boards when she tried to brush Lovelace's thick coat. The cat's whisker she poked down there herself. The drips from her brother Harold's nosebleed behind the sink. Her skin: the dust when the next owner opens the curtains. Will they see her shadow on the path on Midsummer Eve, like the hollow in a mattress, the scuff of her ankle boot where she grabbed Boadicea to put her lead on? The sway of the silver birch is reflected in the looking glass and the Italian scene on the dinner service fills with rain. The lining in the drawers made from the Christmas wrapping paper flutters in the wind and reveals the orange iodine spill in the top drawer. The delivery note in chalk on the bottom of the upside down balloon chair has a Marylebone address on it. The red Moroccan leather copy of *Pilgrim's Progress* spills a lucky four-leaf clover she constructed by adding another leaf. The flattened maidenhair fern from Lake Coniston pokes out the side of the Baedeker of Rome. There is also a postcard of a Thanksgiving turkey in the *Lives of the Saints*, first published in 1290.

Figure 47

St. Margaret of Antioch is the patron saint of childbirth, and the name Margaret means pearl in Sanskrit. It's where the French chemist and inventor of the colour wheel Chevreul got the name for the pearlescent drops of oil he discovered in 1813, that then became the basis of margarine. Cottonseed oil was the key component of the margarine that Hippolyte Mège-Mouriès patents in answer to Napoleon III's plea for cheap butter for the army, navy, and the lower classes. Chevreul's *Cercles Chromatiques* consists of a sequence of 11 colour wheels. The first is divided into 72 pure colours. In the subsequent wheels, ten per cent black is added until the last wheel is completely dark, colourless.

Figure 48

1290 is the 'year without winter' in Britain and Western Europe. Autumn leaves rust and are replaced with soft lime green ones with fresh accordion pleats. No frost touches the haws and the sky does not darken early. Some say it is a punishment from the Jews who, on July 18th, are given the edict of expulsion by King Edward I. Beatrice Portinari dies, aged 25, on a cool day one month earlier, and in the *Divine Comedy* Dante imagines meeting her, his childhood sweetheart in heaven, and her showing him what to expect.

Figure 49

I arrive home from work on my 23rd birthday to find my way blocked by a pile of furniture, tubes of Anusol, divorce papers, my brother-in-law's knighthood certificate, stump socks, cigarette cards, pebbles, Penguin Classics, picnic hampers full of receipts, dining room furniture, my sister's milk expresser, and a relic of St. Agnes. Three of my sisters have received similar piles and I am jealous of the one who got my stuff and the Freemason apron and case.

Figure 50

On her kitchen wall, my mother hung a picture of the Symbolist poet Saint-Pol-Roux. Standing in a garden of hollyhocks and mallow, he is a solid figure with a conjoined apparition. Divine, his daughter, looks like a ghost that has developed on the film. In 1937, on the advice of a clairvoyant, the newly rich poet Saint-Pol-Roux built a manor house over a fisherman's cottage on the volcanic west coast of France. On the night of

June 23rd, 1940, a German soldier broke in and, when confronted by Saint-Pol-Roux and Divine, Divine opened fire. The poet was shot twice, and his housekeeper was killed as she threw herself in front of Divine. The soldier then attempted to rape Divine but was driven away by her alsatian, Felice. Both Saint-Pol-Roux and his Divine survived, but when Saint-Pol-Roux learned, three months later, that the house had been ransacked by the Nazis and his library had been burned he died in the hospital in Brest where he had hereto been recuperating. In 1944, the British bombed the manor house, leaving it in ruins. The ruins revive once a year in July when the fruit and flowers that Saint-Pol-Roux planted for his daughter, return.

There was another postcard of Winston Churchill sitting in a green fringed Lloyd Loom chair in the shade at Chateau de Lourmarin. A card table holds a pickle jar full of stout, squirrel brushes with russet handles. A mahl stick, a silky swathe of Utrillan pastels, and a tightly stretched linen canvas, stolen from the curtain lining of the nursery at Chartwell, rest by his brogues. A Japanese scroll shades the painting: it looks like a pissoir. There is also a tumbler of Scotch, Martini, a breakfast Hock, a Quorum Julieta cigar dunked in brandy, port, a Fedora hat, a scientist's white overalls and another painting that depicts a section of the view.

In the bathroom, my mother chose a wrinkled copy of a Julia Margaret Cameron photograph of Tennyson in a clip frame. My sisters and I all put a towel over it when we get naked, so similar is Tennyson's wiry pubic beard to my father's. Under the beard is a bad oil copy of a Reynolds painting made by my mother. A very hairy baby with a huge cannonball head is held by a woman: his mother. The baby's head is being cradled in the way that Jackie Kennedy held JFK's when his brain fell out in Dallas. The fontanelle is seeping, and the anguished mother is in a helpless crisis. The Poplar trees in the background are indifferent, rustling in the wind. 'Sir Joshua Reynolds used to sign off all of his letters to Nelly O'Brien, "Yours to the hilt" ' my mother says one night in a low voice as she pats me down with a towel, looking at the painting and snorting through her huge nostrils.

A section of Botticelli's *Venus* hangs on my mother's bedroom wall, facing her bed in every house she has lived in. The framed print was given to her by an admirer: the arabesques of her hair reminded him, he said, of hers when she silently served food at the dinner table, her head bent over as she landed a heavy bowl of chilled Vichyssoise before him. The whole image would have shown my mother as Venus in her full nakedness, spherical peach breasts, soft feet unfolding from a giant scallop, waves pulling forwards. My mother and my sister Susannah were often mistaken for each other from behind, their long dense hair folding over their shoulders and ending in a bouncing flick of lady's mantle: the unbridled pelt, the waterfall of fur as rich and dark as a beeswaxed piano.

The bay window housed my mother's desk. I could sit at it, look out, and get a glimpse of the flowerbed and beyond it the pavement, often with one of my mother's chickens standing there trying to get grit from the road. My mother's diary was laid out showing the encrypted writing that I was so embarrassed of when she wrote my school notes. Later I faked it, when I lived on my own. Like Rebecca's desk, prepared for her life as a mistress of a house, it was a three-leaf affair with oak leaf garland handles. It fitted perfectly into the large window near the flowerbed. I had found an earring belonging to one of the house's previous owners in that flowerbed; she had been the first woman in the village to have electricity and had hosted a lot of parties. The earring was shaped like a wedding bouquet, but I don't think she ever married. I hoped that we had slept in the same bedroom and that the earring had been on her dressing table and had flown out of the window with the heavy push of an expensive curtain. Or maybe she cast the wedding bouquet out of the window as she danced into bed with a man. She had inherited money but used it up quickly. She, like my mother, sewed clothes for rich women.

My mother's desk had a range of artefacts on it: heather and a snail shell from Skye petrified inside a glass paperweight. I tried to chip the heather out, but the glass went opaque and I mildly ruined it. There was a bible with a solid silver front. Every time I looked at it I had the same impulse I have with a Bourbon biscuit: to bite the top solid part off the soft papery bit and indeed I had done that when I was five, leaving the bible delicately held together by the immobility of the desk. If a moth had landed near it, it would have disintegrated. I wanted to break my mother's paperweight apart, to find the living breathing truth within. But when I tried to get to the heather which, magnified, looks fresh with ecclesiastical purple flowers, and bubbles of dew upon them, it was just a dried piece of twig fused to the glass forever.

My mother often amused my friends when they came over. She would do handstands at tea parties (in sheer knickers). She would wail if we cut ourselves and run away crying. We would trap spiders for her as she bit her knuckles and whimpered. She would put crisps in the oven until they went soft and call them 'game chips'. She marvelled that we could cook an egg or cut bread. She would slam doors if she was excluded from a midnight feast. She would sleep until midday and faint upside down naked on the stairs. My father would tread carefully over her, his moccasin tassels touching her hair. She had fainted in Harrods food hall too and at a Francis Bacon private view where she clung on to a painting. The gallery assistant had run towards her and peeled her fingers off the frame.

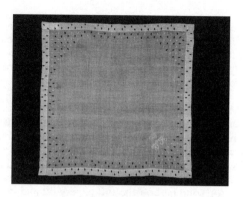

Figure 51

In 1972, Vivien Greene wife of the celebrated author, screenwriter and suspected spy Graham was employed to make an inventory of the Nuremberg dolls at Monkton House. The house belonged to art collector Edward James who was in Mexico with his eighteen parrots and twelve pythons, washing naked in the waterfalls at Las Pozos surrounded by the concrete palm trees.

At night, Vivien read about Alexander Pope's grotto, how he shot a stalactite from the roof of Wookey Hole. She had enjoyed an account of animal husbandry in the 1700s: a Dorset farmer writes in his diary 'My old dog Quon was killed and baked for his grease, which yielded 11 lb'. She no longer wants to read the book and instead, lies on her bed and looks at the ceiling. She wakes up cold and the wrens she has grown used to hearing are silent. She looks out of one of the seven windows that surround her bed. There is a coverlet of snow on the garden. She wanders the house barefoot, agog at its ethereal order. James' bedroom is cool and elegant, and smells of basilica incense. The house was designed by Lutyens and came into being in 1902 along with Tallulah Bankhead, Charles Lindbergh, Ogden Nash and Leni Riefenstahl.

Pevsner is born this year too in Leipzig. He admires the cultural and economic policies of the young Adolf Hitler and says that 'There are worse things than Hitlerism'. He travels to Monkton House which he thinks is one of the things that is worse than Hitlerism. Pevsner writes for information about the house to the poet John Betjeman who tells him: 'Shortly before the war Mrs. Willy James' son, Edward Frank Willis James had a house in the woods designed by Dali. It was in the shape of a womb and inside it was lined with fur. There were curves in the shape of Mae West's lips. I wonder if it is still there.'

Vivien beholds Edward James' bed as a mirage. It is a replica of Nelson's funeral car; luscious plumes of carved ostrich feathers hold the canopy of carved, gold and pink Egyptian cherrywood. Pongee mourning dress curtains hang at each corner and the interior is a flushed peach tulle of the type his wife Tilly Losch had worn ruched up in curves on her soft pink nipples. Vivien imagines how it must feel to rest a hot cheek on these soft swagged ripples. There are two globes, two lips, two lamps with emu feet, and a Venetian depth pole with a swirl of red and white swizzled up its length that then holds a candle that is lit every night. The bed she sleeps on is curved like the arch of a spine, the ceiling above her is shot glass, sprinkled with golden stars that awaken as a celestial illumination at night. The walls are eau de nil velvet. The bathroom is made entirely of Portuguese rose marble and looks like the Amber Room in the Catherine Palace. James' bathroom is as pale and smooth as single cream. There is a collage that Vivien knows is by Leonora Carrington. In the marbled inventory book the title is listed as *Foundress of the Sisterhood of the Holy Little Jumping Virgins*. Wraithlike figures gather in a discarnate landscape and Hero Twins cast a visitor in a boat off to the underworld.

Vivien hears the dogs bark downstairs, laughter, and the door opens; Edward James has made a return from Mexico. Sitting in Mae West's huge lips Vivien beholds the man: Edward James, a bonfire, a double bass, a very large bear. The walls are padded pale pink leather and studded with buttons; it is like falling into a giant blushing Chesterfield. From her cold house in Oxfordshire, years later, Vivienne makes a model of Magritte's *La Reproduction Interdite* using her daughter's watered-down poster paints to go on the wall of a miniature version of Monkton that she calls *The Toll House*. Cutting a piece out of a Turnbull and Asser charmeuse silk handkerchief she unrolls the edges. It smells of Jicky and was a present to her husband from Lady Catherine Walston. She prods the silk down the back of the miniature Mae West lips sofa with her unpicker. Her husband is in Capri.

Figure 52

Doctor Frances Glessner Lee is sitting in her townhouse in Quincy, Harvard. She puts the paintbrush with school blue Indian ink in her cup of lukewarm tea. She turns the radio up and then down again when she hears them talking about the debut of the bikini again. Why can't they see that naming a bathing suit after an Atomic bomb site is ridiculous? She draws the curtain back as far as it will go to let more light in. These models later become known as the Nutshell Studies of Unexplained Death and throughout the 1940s and 1950s are used to test police officers on their detective skills. Glessner adds the effects of cyanosis (blue cheeks) to the woman's face with a brush dusted in cobalt blue watercolour. She turns the small head in her hands and wonders if she needs to add two more tiny lumps of modelling clay to the eyes, to give the impression of bulging. She checks to see if the paint on the miniature baby's cot is dry enough to add the embroidered quilt or not.

Figure 53

Anna Atkins and her cousin Bunny look at the blue photographic paper in the sun. As they wash the chemicals off the paper with a huge bowl of cold water, Amalie von Ranke, wife of Alfred Graves, an Irish schools' inspector, gives birth to her fifth child. At the age of seven the child has double pneumonia and measles and almost dies. Later he gets stabbed through his lung and suffers from Spanish influenza just before he is demobbed. No one knows that the Prussian blue chemicals will be turned into Zyklon B or used in the apple that Alan Turing bites into to kill himself after he is caught cottaging, that 900 people will drink them in Flavor Aid at the Jonestown massacre of 1978, that Rommel, Eva Braun, Himmler, Göring and Hitler's dog, Blondie, will take them in glass capsules to die. They will be used to kill the cicadas and locusts in the citrus groves of California, then prisoner Gee Jon. Gee loses consciousness after five seconds, his head continuing to nod up and down for six minutes. He is completely motionless after ten minutes. Some of the witnesses said they thought they could smell almond blossom as he died.

Figure 54

In 1985, serial killer Leonard Lake dies in custody after having ingested cyanide pills he had sewn into his clothes. Five lionesses at the Singapore Zoo are put on birth control. Dian Fossey is found murdered in scrubland in Rwanda and Robert Graves is found dead on the cold floor tiles of his bathroom in Spain. And after reading that it is one of Sylvia Plath's favourite pastimes along with drinking sherry and sunbathing, I am ten and having a hot bath in the room where I host my Nature Show.

Figure 55

The Victorian slipper bath has my grandfather's hoist above it and a cork step for a makeshift plinth for jars of mosquito larvae, fake owl pellets that I had made from used cotton wool, pencil shavings, and other traces of nature I could find in the suburbs of Liverpool near where my family live. I place one of the many period stained sheets, a sheet produced by six women, over the bath. Often the Nature Show leaves traces: large striped garden spiders, mosquitoes, mould and damp from the artefacts I had found in the River Mersey that abutted our house. My mother and sisters often come and talk about where my father has gone, my mother teary-eyed and raw, her face a shattered plate, poorly glued. She lights a cigarette and shares it with my elder sisters. The earwigs wake up from their cold stupor and creep into the crevices behind water pipes and overflow holes. My mother and sisters use words I only vaguely understand and I try and remember to look them up in the dictionary in my father's out of bounds study: 'neurotic,' 'cash,' 'mistress,' 'possessive,' 'obsessed,' 'quim.' Sometimes the warmth of a bath invites the insects back and I remember a particularly terrifying Monday winter evening when I was stuck in the slipper as a cloud of daddy long-legs puffed out of a dark corner and landed elegantly on the roll edge like the pilots of Pussy Galore's Flying Circus. In my latest Nature Club, I show an example of a dog rose. Cut in the wrong way a cultivated rose returns to its natural wild ancestor.

In the morning when I was the only one awake - when the birds started to sing over the containers in the docks next door, when the container ships blew their horns over the Mersey - I'd look at the things in my room. Jemima the doll had frustrating hands, each was made from one piece of fabric and the fingers were sewn lines, like the Citroën ambulance car with the doors that wouldn't open and my Clothkits dress with fake pockets. My grandmother's arthritic hands were the same. Holding her hand was like holding the hand of a shop dummy or an oven glove.

The Boobly Oobly was my favourite toy. If I woke up early on Sunday and couldn't go back to sleep, I would think about what look I might give it that day. I'd look at my sisters' wall: Grace Jones, Buzby, Faye Dunnaway in *Bonnie and Clyde*, the one with the dark hair in Charlie's Angels, Rowan Atkinson, Eliot Gould, 'Hot Lips' Houlihan, Anthony Andrews as Sebastian Flyte with Aloysius the bear. We didn't have a TV, but we had a deal with our neighbours, Luke and Andrew, that they would push their TV close to the window, and my sisters and I would stand on the roof wearing hats and cagoules in the rain to see it. I had to wait until the afternoon to get Boobly Oobly and I could only get her at certain times of the year. It wasn't until we had games day at school, and I saw Barbies, Etch A Sketch and Weebles, that I realised that Boobly Oobly only really had appeal for me. I felt shame when I she was delivered to me in a tea towel on Sunday afternoons after that. I now think of Boobly Oobly when making

Robert Carrier's minestrone soup, because Boobly Oobly was an overripe marrow, a parsnip or a sugar beet that I put lipstick on.

My dollhouse contained fragments of my grandmother's William Morris Blackthorn print, taking on an overwhelming, but comforting, psychedelic scale in the miniature sitting room. The dollhouse father could never relax. He couldn't bend his legs, so I laid him on the chaise longue in the sitting room next to the pipe-cleaner cat. He was at the mercy of the botanical wallpaper and its powerful supine curves, lying in a never-ending hypnogogic trance.

One afternoon, a woman came to the porch door of our house in Liverpool. Mother said she had hair the colour of 'Butterscotch Angel Delight'. The woman said she had come because of a piece of paper she had found in a library book. She left laughing and said it was a delight to meet a man as charming as my father. 'Cheap perfume' said my father as he shut the door and took out a tin of panatelas from the breast pocket of his tweed jacket.

*

My grandmother Mikey's herbarium was made from alpine plants. On the first day of lent, 1951, in her house on the Isle of Wight, while my grandfather was away at a conference in New York, and her children were at boarding school, she told the chauffeur, Raoul, to drive her to Switzerland. He was unable to contact my grandfather who at the time was buying my grandmother a bracelet from Saks. Then followed her herbarium, the asylum, and her first of 32 sessions of ECT. Nobody wanted the herbarium but me: the frail, tissue like gentians, the edelweiss crackling and perishing with age. Today she would be diagnosed as bipolar, then she was termed hysterical. She wore black underwear when she was energetic and went on huge spending forays buying plants and flowers: Jersey for narcissi, the woods of Cornwall for sweet violets. I thought of her when I heard of the story of Narcissus staring at his beautiful reflection in the pool, and how Freud would not have helped her either. After her back, legs and arms were broken, her lungs punctured, her jaw shattered, and the grandson that was sitting on her lap killed, she took trunks of lilies home to the UK in the ambulance from what was then my mother's garden in Uganda, having wrapped them in silk headscarves she had drenched in water. There are photographs of her in the private ambulance, holding the lilies in a headscarf, like a newly born baby.

The caramel coloured roses from Mikey's garden used to loll in cut glass cornets. She showed me how to make flower arrangements when I was a child. I won prizes at school, at the Liverpool Show, and when I was seven at the South Suffolk Show. My mother made me present the flower arrangements and the cups that I won at the Liverpool Show to my father. He would leave them where I put them until the water in the arrangement container (usually a shell) stank of cabbage. My mother left them there, unable to reach that part of the room for all the newspapers in their geological piles. My father would never remove them either; he'd cover them with more newspapers. After a year, I would have to burrow under my father's things to retrieve the cup. Once I had the humiliation of not being able to find the cup at all. Two years later I found it trodden on in my father's wardrobe, under his dirty jockstrap pile.

My mother said my grandmother taught her nothing useful, only things about dogs and plants. 'I'm on heat' my mother had said to Matron as the hot blood trickled out of her. At boarding school my mother placed her hairbrush next to the whimsy of a badger, and a photograph of her mother, father and brother in a mosaic enamel frame on the bedside cabinet, with fat white sanitary towels in the drawer below.

Figure 56

Anna Atkins looks at the fish on the pale blue plate. Plaice start life with eyes on either side of their face, then one eye travels to join the other and stays there. She sees, under the melting butter, the path the moving eye took on the fish's skin. Anna is in bed. She squints one eye to focus on the words of her newspaper. She knows she will live maybe one or two more days. The astrantias in the Waterford Crystal vase by her bed will outlive her, but she still feels compelled to know about the world. To marinate in it and float out into it, a full treacle soaked sponge not an empty husk. She would like to have died on her birthday, a neat circle, like Rafael and Shakespeare, but as in all things she lacks forethought.

She reads an article by the frightful Henry Labouchère:

> *Yesterday, I had a slice of Pollux for dinner. Pollux and his brother Castor are two elephants, which have been killed. It was tough, coarse, and oily, and I do not recommend English families to eat elephant as long as they can get beef or mutton.*

He goes on to mention rat and *Cuissot de Loup, Sauce Chevreuil* (Haunch of Wolf With a Deer Sauce) and *Chameau Rôti à l'Anglaise* (Camel Roasted With an English Sauce). Champion racehorses were being eaten in Paris too. Only the lions and tigers survived because they were too fearsome and the monkeys because they were too human. The rest of the zoo in the Jardin de Plantes had been consumed.

Poor Castor and Pollux, thinks Anna. I would so like to meet them in heaven and apologise, and also to my mother for killing her by being born. And what is the English sauce that comes with the camel?

Figure 57

III

One of my older sisters, Susannah, got out her Flower Fairies folder. 'I've got really nice paper for this week's SOS. Granny Eavis gave it to me and I thought we could add a pressed flower. Maybe some vetch from Wales.'

We wrote the same thing that we always wrote. Susannah had the nicest handwriting and she was good at organising things. She and Esther were both head girls at their school later, and my mother had been too. That's why it was bad that my mother got pregnant by the English teacher at 17 and why she had to move to Uganda. My sister had her hair done like Princess Anne for the head girl photo and the silk shirt she wore matched the peach lemon roses (*Rosa Peace*) on the table next to her folded hands.

'Please help us,' it said.

'Ormiston,
'Hadassah Grove,
'Sefton Park,
'Liverpool.'

'Please only talk to any young girl if you come. No adults.'

We signed our names in a circle like the Quakers did, and it formed a garland of hope. Esther got out the pile of library books, and we found the best bit in each book. The bit where they put daisies in their pubic hair was a good bit, we decided, for *Lady Chatterley's Lover* and we put the note in there. The writing was miniature, like the note that the mice leave in the *Tailor of Gloucester* to ask for more cherry silk twist.

Figure 58

"My name is Margaret Clay, I am eight and I live at number 18 Kensington Park Gardens. I go to St Paul's School for girls and my father is Sir George Felix Neville Clay, 5th Baronet. My best drawing at the moment is one of a black mamba coiled and ready to attack a mongoose. I was eight just after the New Year which is 1903 but I haven't got used to it yet and I keep writing 1902 in my book which Mrs Constance says is very silly.

It was freezing cold the morning my youngest sister was born, and I could see my breath while I sat up in bed. Later when she grew, she had thick, heavy hair that felt like a horse's mane. Her skin was smooth and freckleless. Her legs, when tanned, had blonde down on them that grew in circular patches like wind swirls on a sand dune. Her teeth were square and healthy and her nails short and clean. She never wore shoes unless made to and would float in the bath for hours in a trance like, she said, the Lady of Shallot. She meant Ophelia.

She was 11 when our cousin, the war hero Colonel Meinertzhagen, CBE, DSO, came to stay. He wrote about us in his diaries. He said he had dreamt about my sister when she was born. He had a photo my mother gave him of us doing eurhythmics in the orchard. From boyhood, he had been in tune with nature; he made drawings and described to us the sound of rain on leaves in the rainforests and the glitter sparkle of snowy mountains. He discovered new species of bats and birds. He knew all about bird lice too and how sometimes the lice make the birds go crazy. He was a chairman of important societies and there was a room that had been named after him in the Natural History Museum. He was more than a war hero, he was a spy. He knew Charles Darwin when he was a little boy and Oscar Wilde and he had been to Mesopotamia and deep in the bush of Africa where he met the King of Saxony and was roommates with Lawrence of Arabia. He killed and stuffed a giant African forest hog and sent it back to England, where it was named after him, *Hylochoerus Meinertzhageni*. Later, he discovered the Afghan snowfinch. It lives in the northern parts of the Hindu Kush and makes its nest on the ground, lining it with hair. He named it after my sister, *Montifringilla Theresae*. Then he named a bird he found in Morocco after her too *Riparia Rupestris Theresa*, and ten others after that."

Figure 59

"They said Colonel Meinertzhagen's second wife shot herself in the head in the highlands in a terrible accident. My sister became quiet and stayed living at the family home at Kensington Gardens. At least she could visit the Natural History Museum I thought, but she never left the house. The Colonel paid for an underground tunnel to be built to connect his house next door to ours . My mother never spoke to the Colonel directly after that, always through someone else, even if he was in the room. He wrote his diary on loose leafed paper and they found the paper was different on the entry when he had written about making fun of Hitler to his face and the archivist cataloguing his work wondered when he had written it. The diaries are still in the Bodleian Library. He rediscovered a forest owlet (*Athene Blewitti*) after it had been extinct for 70 years. In 1995, the Natural History Museum experts at Tring analysed all the specimens that he'd donated and discovered they were stuffed with the same cotton as the specimens that had been stolen from the museum in 1952."

Figure 60

In 1850 Florence Nightingale saved a baby owl from some boys who were tormenting it in Athens, smuggled it home, and christened it Athena. To be persuaded to enter a cage, the owl had to be mesmerised, but she soon became a devoted companion. She would perch on her mistress's finger for feeds as well as bow and curtsy on a table. On hearing of Florence's imminent departure for the Crimea, the family left Athena shut in an attic. Starved of the attention she craved, the owl, it seems, died of a fit, leaving her owner heartbroken.

Figure 61

The Fitzwilliam Museum in Cambridge keeps a tall owl punchbowl in its basement. It was cracked in the San Francisco earthquake of 1922. Later, on the day of the earthquake, my grandmother Mikey bought my grandfather some pyjamas. She liked the word 'pyjamas' - both Urdu and Persian - and she felt that though he would dislike them, they would help her feel more in control in the bedroom.

*

The Mary Rose was being pulled from her seabed in Portsmouth and I was lying in my pyjamas under the cat, getting hot. I was off school because it was PE that day and because my mother was lonely. I was colouring in a scene in my Gideon's bible. My father said we could defile that book and no other because it had religious mush in it, and it was free. I was adding red pencil to one of the nuns wearing high heels, smoking cigarettes, and drinking out of champagne saucers, when my mother called me urgently. I wondered if she had cut herself. Often, she would faint, and we would have to cover her eyes quickly with something, a jumper or a hanky. Once I placed a black tulip petal over each eye so she couldn't see the wound. Oddly, if she cut herself on a rose or doing something in the garden and hadn't seen it, she would merely say 'Oh have I?' Like you had offended her by pointing out she had a huge glistening ruby streak on her hands or face. She'd absent mindedly take the (blue) silk scarf off her head and wind it around her earthy fingers; frowning as she talked about supper and what food we had in the house. Usually there was an ugly potato left in the muddy paper sack, sometimes the water would be boiling, and I'd wash the potato to find it was only a lump of soil. Then there was just Ryvita and margarine and sometimes cress. My sister grew cress on an old soft nappy we used to have for comfort. It was called Terry the Nap. Sometimes there was my father's *patum peperium* if it was near Christmas and we were careful how we took off a layer with the knife. My eldest sister showed us a technique that involved patting the edges down with a cotton wool bud and building a false wall.

*

My mother yelped with excitement and the dog gulped and wagged her tail and ran towards her. The cat jumped off my bed. I saw her sandy tail aloft and her pink anus disappear downstairs. There was a little boy on the esplanade on the patch of grass where I played with my Native American play people. He was in a blue cardigan and a *Star Wars* tee-shirt, the kind my boyfriend Philip had worn at my birthday party and my mother had called cheap. Later she said that Philip's whole family had square heads and my sister agreed. The little boy was wet all over and was strapped into a mud filled pram. His shoes must have been ruined. His mother and his sister had been rescued at Birkenhead. He had been pulled down by the weight of the pram. The police put a tent up on the Navajo Plains. It looked like it was made of bin bags and was like the ones the electricity people put up but a different shape and not striped. It reminded me of the black uniforms SS guards wore in films, and the door flapped open like a large leather lapel. People crouched down and went in and out of it wearing the same suits the Rentokil people wore when they killed the rats. Each rat was inflated except one that was in perfect condition. She had dried out like a kestrel in an Egyptian tomb and I kept her for several years under a Tiny Tears pillow, her whiskers stuck out behind Baby Louise's blonde plait in the wicker pram with the seersucker curtains. I never told my friends when they pushed the dolls around. The rat only got discovered when I hid a quarter of a packet of custard creams. I don't like the taste of the biscuits, but I like the embossed fern croziers that pattern them.

At night, I lay on my mother, her heartbeat was so much slower than mine. She told me that the body got copied like a drawing with carbon paper every few years and each time the drawing gets weaker and weaker. Humans come from the stars and return to the stars. She'd stroke my ears and leave a nightlight candle burning. All the different organs had to work together and if one gave up it could be patched up with another person's and then Guardian reading vegetarians suddenly woke up wanting a beef burger and with a love of Margaret Thatcher's ankles. My father was a Guardian reading vegetarian. I woke up in total blackness and my mother had gone.

The sound of gunshot often came at about 5 am. It only happened when our labrador Biscuit was on heat and her blonde thighs turned pink. My father would be sitting naked by the upstairs sitting room window. That's when he shot Rufous, the red setter that belonged to the Nightingales, a neighbouring family that consisted of a surgeon, his uptight wife, and their beautiful daughters. We weren't allowed to say this when we went for a dinner party at their house. The chocolate mousse was delicious just like the one in *Rosemary's Baby* and I was scared to eat it. Then I thought about it and realised I didn't care. I knew about things like that and I'd prefer to be unconscious when it happened anyway. The Nightingale father had tried quickly to save Rufous he said by sewing him up. 'What does Rufous mean?' I said, knowing because it was one of the crossword questions my father had written. He'd cut out squared paper at night and lay it on the floor to make his own concise crossword. In the morning, the curtains would be closed and there'd be the leftovers of a drum of rollmops. Coins from his pocket would have fallen down the side of the sofa and lots of screwed up paper lay in piles on the rug. It was like an angry otter had been dwelling there. He was furious if we guessed any of his answers. In the end the man at *The Times* sacked him anyway because he'd said the Anglo-Saxon word to his wife. I shared my father's guilt because I'd kicked the Nightingale's tortoise Balthazar, to see what he'd do. 'It means red, like your hair. Mr. Rufous had hair just as glorious as yours.'

Figure 62

It is 30th September, 1888, and Elizabeth Stride's body has just been found wearing a posy of a pale pink rose and a sprig of maidenhair fern and holding in her left hand a throat lozenge. She is later suspected of being the first victim of Jack the Ripper. Van Gogh cuts off part of his ear, and the Brighton Beach Hotel in Coney Island, New York is moved 520 feet using six steam locomotives to save it from the lash of the sea. The hotel is an easy walk away from one of Dreamlands most popular exhibits: 'All the World Loves a Baby' says the sign above the incubators, where for 25 cents you can see the tiny breathing babies inside their glass cases. Leopold Blaschka and his son Rudolph Blaschka are making 847 life size glass plants for Harvard University. The Blaschka's have been glassmakers and jewellers since the 15th century. More lifelike and more painstaking than a Dutch still life, these glass botanical specimens feature decaying leaves and blossoms, visiting bees and fungal infections. These plants are neither scientific (too singularly perfect to study) nor art (too much like copies to be anything other than kitsch). These objects, designed to aid classification of species, are themselves hard to classify. Originally called 'scientific models,' now referred to as 'the glass flowers' their role has subtly changed since conception. The models rarely leave Harvard, when they do, they are transported by hearse.

The Blaschkas counterfeited botanical forms and modelled jellied delights: ruby petals, sapphire stamens and the crosier of an emerald fern. When visitors such as the Queen of Sweden came to visit Rudolph in his workshop, she was amazed that he worked in temperatures of 95 degrees with the windows and doors sealed so that no flicker of air could disturb the flame used to manipulate the glass. Many others tried to visit and commission plants for themselves, or to discover the 'secret' method of making these objects.

In 1941, a professor at Harvard heard of the bombing of Pearl Harbour and made the glass plant cases bombproof. Pilgrims still visit the glass flowers and are instructed to walk softly, to breathe gently, and to stay, as with the reptile house at London Zoo, away from the glass. The glass plants of South America, the Royal Gardens of Pillnitz and of the Blaschkas' own garden at Hosterwitz are still growing in cabinets at Harvard's Botanical Museum.

Figure 63

Before she leaves for London Anna Atkins flattens the mullein leaf. She had tried sleeping with some under her pillow, but it did nothing to reduce her bad dreams. As a child, she and Anne knew it brought back other children kidnapped by the fairies, and they kept a sticky wick rolled from the hairs on its leaves by each of their beds in case the other was taken. A necromancer's plant, it had been mentioned in the recent Bridget Cleary case. Beautiful, educated, and childless, Bridget Cleary's neighbours realised she was a changeling and that they must retrieve her soul from the fairies of Kylnagranagh ringfort by dosing her with Mullein. She died the next day and the unionist newspapers called the villagers, 'savages'. Anna wraps the prints in brown paper, wondering if this is how a nursemaid dresses a baby in a nappy. Her hands are smudged with Prussian blue. Unseen until morning, developing in the daylight before she wakes, the dirty secret is locked into her hands, Lady Macbeth like for days: a blue midwife in the night.

Anna knows how to get to the Linnaean Society, the Royal Society, and Albertopolis, the nickname given to Exhibition Road. In the past she has waited to meet her father outside each of these institutions that she will visit again today, placing her arm through his as they walked away afterwards. A milkwood seed is sucked into the train carriage from the marsh outside. She goes to grab it to make a wish, but it dodges her and floats through the open sliding door, deeper down the train corridor. A damsel fly buzzes in and out of the window. Rosebay willowherb, buddleia from China, and thistles swing in the wind outside. A vixen is curled around itself like a cat in the sun on the railway sidings. Her eyes cautiously looking out from behind her feather duster like brush as the train passes her noisily. Anna's string bag, wicker basket, portmanteau, and card portfolio rest on the velvet seat opposite her.

The train arrives at London Bridge. Anna's face is grey from the smoke and she wipes it with spit and a hanky in the convenience glass. The volumes of cyanotypes are in the basket covered with a cloth in case of rain and look like fresh bread for the poor. When she reaches each institution, she goes through the same ritual and describes why her donation would mean so much to her father. She waits outside as they nod their heads and take the packages, usually a librarian she has never met before. At the Royal Institute, there is speckle of sleet and she is invited into the hall where she stands on the black and white chequered floor tiles, wondering whether to remove her gloves or not and wishing she had put powder on her face to counteract the cold flush of carmine she feels spreading across her cheeks and moistening her nose. She tries to explain to the assistant, Mr. Soames, why she is giving him these prints. He reassures her that her father's previous letter had explained her desire to present a gift in the future and that Herschel has taken her under his wing. They ask after her husband at the Linnean Society. She wonders what they will do with the prints and how long they will keep them, if they keep them at all. They enjoyed the memoir of her father and were glad she had written it. Did she enjoy it? Yes, she said, just as she enjoyed writing her novels too. He seemed not to hear, or if he did to understand this comment. Perhaps he knew not of her other books.

Figure 64

In 2012, the librarian in the Linnean Society said the highlight of her job was collecting the mallow, the Scarlet Pimpernel, and the speedwell on her walk from her garden to Swiss Cottage tube station. Wrapped in kitchen foil with a soggy plug of cotton wool at its base, she wound it with thread whilst sitting on the train. She filled the glass tumbler with water from the library kitchen, snipping and arranging the flowers before she had put down her handbag. Placing them at Linnaeus' feet, she said, reminded her of Sunday School and the jobs she and her sisters were given by the Church Warden. Among postcards from fellow librarians, bookmarks and a list of how staff liked their tea, Sylvia found my pile of Anna Atkins' volumes. She wheeled them out on a trolley and left me to sit down and look at them, resting them on a sapphire blue, velvet cushion.

Figure 65

London did smell today, Anna thinks, but not as badly as the Great Stink of 1858. Joseph Bazalgette father of 11 children, who suffered a nervous breakdown when designing the railways, has been called upon to design sewers that will solve the problem first identified by John Snow. Joseph Bazalgette will later become the great-grandfather of Ian Willoughby Bazalgette, known as Baz. Baz will recover from tuberculosis at the Royal Sea Bathing Hospital, Margate before going on to train as a Pilot Officer in 1940. The Victoria Cross he will win posthumously is now on display in the RAF Museum, Hendon beside the goggles of a kamikaze pilot. His aunt, Maureen, will hear of his death after she has recovered from being taken on a stretcher to St.

Thomas' Hospital during the Blitz. 20 years later this stretcher, along with many others, will then be made into a fence outside Rockingham council flats, Southwark. Maureen will walk past the stretcher on her way to the library but won't see it.

Figure 66

The pipes Joseph Bazalgette designs are laid by navvies from County Carshall and won't have to be repaired until 2013, the morning that Margaret Thatcher dies in her bed at the Ritz. Soon after Michael Winner almost dies after eating bad oysters, and Esther Williams dies in her sleep, in LA. Her ashes are scattered in the Pacific Ocean. Fatberg, 15 tonnes of human waste, lard and wet wipes flushed down UK toilets grows so big that it cracks the pipes and threatens to push itself out of the manholes in Kingston.

Figure 67

On the April 15th 1912 survivors of RMS Titanic describe to the band playing *Abide With Me* as the ship sinks into the North Atlantic Ocean. The first instrument discovered amongst the wreckage in 1985 is the piano 24 year old Theodore Ronald Brailey from Walthamstow played. His body was never discovered and remains on the seabed with the rest of the Titanic. Edith Cavell also sings *Abide With Me* while interned in a German prison in 1915, the evening before she is shot.

Figure 68

When he gets off the plane at LaGuardia airport in Queens, New York, on November 22nd 1963, Richard Nixon takes a taxi into Manhattan. At a red light, the driver of another taxi shouts, 'Hey did you hear that Kennedy's been assassinated?' Later, when he sees the footage of the coffin being wheeled from the plane it looks like a fish kettle.

Richard Nixon sits down at the end of the dining table with the unnecessary slippery cloth. He looks at the ham, new potatoes, and sliced watery green beans. He picks up the fork but can't feel it. He can't feel anything apart from the warm flood of urine in his pants. After a stroke his brain shuts down and he slithers into a coma. He dies at 9:08 P.M. on April 22nd, 1994. *Abide With Me* is played at his funeral.

Figure 69

Gravy Browning was in the garden being raped by the huge black and white cat we called Ernest Hemingway. Gravy Browning was named after a huge panda teddy my sister Susannah had tried to win for me at Otterspool. Susannah was brilliant at shooting and she hit the box of smarties five times and still it wouldn't fall over. 'It's made of concrete' one of my other sisters, Hannah, had said and then my sister Ruth did a jump like you would onto an inflatable bed in a swimming pool and tried to grab it. 'It's nailed on!' she shouted victoriously. The boy behind the range came out and punched her in the eye and told her to fuck off. All of my sisters ran off apart from Esther because she had me on her shoulders. 'You're a cretin,' Esther said to the boy. It was the worst thing we were called at home. He looked mystified. I had finished gnawing off the string that held the giant red sugar dummy from the ceiling by then and we went to find Ruth, my sister with the black eye. She sucked the dummy silently till we'd walked the eight miles home. It was the size of a baby's dummy by the time we reached the Esplanade. We walked up the steps and opened the door. She put a finger in her mouth and pulled out a bright red glassy nipple. She put it in my mouth, and I swallowed it.

Figure 70

After delivering the final volume of cyanotypes to the Linnean Society Anna Atkins walks past Fortnum and Mason. She sees a young girl with hair tied back in golden ringlet cocoons. They bounce with a high sheen and sensuality that belongs in a seraglio. Anna thinks of the triangle of hair at the base of her husband John's back. Like a mermaid, when wet it forms a single pattern that would be called a shingle in the 1930s when Eva Braun had one and a marcel wave when Veronica Lake shook her golden waterfall some decades later. Later, by the time Andy Warhol was drawing the oscillatory waves of hair on his lover's feet, it was called a finger perm. The pattern looks like marks made by a rake through snow, fingers drawn through cream, a fork on a linen tablecloth. It is this thought of the hair at the base of her husband's back that makes Anna write 'Abide With Me' in her letter to him. It is this letter, received three months later at the plantation in Honduras, that makes him return to Kent.

*

When I was almost 13 years old my mother moved to Vatican City, Rome to mend papal robes. My father disappeared. My sisters were at university. My mother left me a copy of her signature so that I could fake school letters and I moved into Canon Sherlock's house. The Canon had died two weeks previously. The shape of his body was still imprinted on the ticking sheet upstairs: a well like the dip made for water in flour for pastry in the mattress. His rubbish was still in the bin, mostly paper and pelargonium heads. Maybe he had given up eating? Radio Four was on but turned down. Soon I adopted his habits. From a very strict upbringing to no rules at all I started to live like the 91 year-old dead Canon. The ship was waiting for a new captain and I was it. Tinned peaches in syrup next to Birds powdered custard. I made the obvious connection, tried them together and liked them: post-war treats for a child born in 1975. I turned the radio up and enjoyed Humphrey Lyttelton on *I'm Sorry I Haven't a Clue* as well as several other radio programmes. I read *The Times* that came through the door for a while, over several days. As I did with *Lolita*, *Pnin* and the poems of Robert Graves. The cat seemed to accept me as the new master. There were drawers and drawers of things, even a table that I discovered had false pockets that opened and yielded a silver dinner service asleep on cobalt velvet beds.

Figure 71

Wine stains on the wall
The rope by the stairs shiny with grease
A carved fireplace that had belonged in the first
Lloyds bank
Bulbs in the spring

The threadbare cat used to pee by the fireplace, and I guessed its name began with E - 'Worm E' it said in a seven-year-old engagement diary - and he was known to me as 'Epuss' and 'Mr E' even after I found out that he was called Edgeware several years after he died. Epuss or Mr E brought a copper pipe slowworm in from the compost heap and briefly returned to the kitten he had once been before the excitement killed him. Along the corridor there were portraits of past Sherlocks, dark etchings with spaniel sideburn wigs. A statue of Christ hung on the wall at the end of the landing and gave the impression that you were having an out of body experience as you mounted the stairs. The dark diamond leaded windows peered out from under the spiders' webs, slugs, snails, caterpillars, and moths that lived in the overhanging thatch. I never knew what nationality, sex or person I was until I lived there and became a recently deceased Canon.

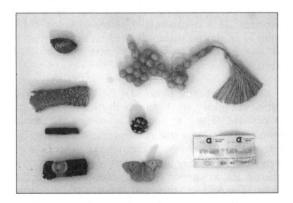

Figure 72

'Irish!' says the porter pushing me through the corridors.

'No, more boring than that, but my grandmother was Danish.'

I lie down on the bed as he wheels me past the noticeboards with photos of babies and thank you cards on. Stunned looking parents, some holding twins, and older children by birthday cakes.

'Where were you born?' says the doctor.

'Liverpool.'

'I love Liverpool.' He sings, '*You'll Never Walk Alone*'. He straps my arms down flat to the gurney and my waist too. He picks up a green cloth apron, 'This goes over your kolpos.'

'Vagina!' the nurse corrects him.

He wraps the masonic shroud around me like a nappy. He's still singing.

'Yassas' I say to the nurse.

'You speak Greek?'

'Only a few words in Greek.' I say, but I realise I'm already dreaming and the ice cold anaesthetic turns into the cream of an eclair in the fridge.

I dream of my father driving and I'm behind him in the Peugeot. He's been invited to my nephew's Bar Mitzvah. 'He's a paedophile,' I try to shout but my mouth is as dry as autumn leaves and it whispers out and sounds like 'Bonbon,' the first French word I learnt.

There are bright lights and I'm awake, wearing a seatbelt strapped very firmly to my stomach. I scratch the cannula. 'There is something wrong, we need an English speaker to explain,' says the nurse. Her huge eyelashes cast shadows on her cheeks. There's a mint green jockstrap on my blanket. The nurse picks it up and I realise it's a surgeon's mask. She looks at me and laughs. 'You told us you loved children when you were asleep. "Paidiá filia", you whispered as we cut your womb. You said it in Greek.'

Figure 73

In October 1976, asked to name three books he had been reading, Nabakov listed a translation of Dante's *Inferno*, an illustrated guide to North American butterflies, and a book of his own: 'the not-quite-finished manuscript of a novel'. Recovering from illness he had, in his febrile state been reading his not-quite-finished book aloud to an audience of 'peacocks, pigeons, my long dead parents, two cypresses, several young nurses crouching around, and a family doctor so old as to be almost invisible.'

*

I drive past Kettle's Yard. The artist-in-residence recently made a porcelain squid for the bath, placed wildflowers on the bed, and toadstools in the cupboard. Jim Ede's aesthetic needed, she felt, to be thwarted by nature. His latent homosexuality so closely protected by the current volunteers is sublimated throughout the house. Now, like Ophelia, his bed is a resting place. The artist placed a small pornographic image of a vigorous youth, T.E. Lawrence, the object of Ede's affection, between the webbing of the bed base, to be found, and no doubt concealed, by conservators later.

Figure 74

Later that day I find myself in another house's garden with weeds at least as high as six feet. There is a man in underpants thrashing them down. It's five A.M. in a village near Cambridge, famous for Moses the giant, who was rumoured to cut off the heads of bad children and replace them with a cabbage. The man's underpants are white and worn and have a rip down the back. He is wearing flip-flops too. It's misty and I planned only to check to see if he was still alive. I can see a crossword with my sister and my initials written in a circle on the side in Parker pen calligraphic script. The man must be in his 70s. He has a paunch and a huge fuzz of white hair and beard. He looks as though his face has been shaved out in the middle. He has a low stoop and walks through the house with the bandy gait of a baboon. He opens the door and I introduce myself, 'Your daughter.' He knows which one because of my hair colour, he says. He is religious now. He talks about Venice; it is his spiritual home. I sit on a pouf with a gash in its side. It always was too pumped up, like a swollen sheep belly. Gabriel Oak must have come along and stabbed it in the stomach I thought.

Figure 75

The only recognition I can feel is with the objects in his house. The Moroccan leather pouf that I sit on puffed out with sawdust and extruded shreds of French newspaper from the 1950s, feels instantly familiar to me and connects with the physical memory of my five year-old self. There is a photograph of me sitting on it, a flat croissant of leather, with my red hair: the fact that makes me sure it is me. The corner cupboard that had never been attached to any wall remains on the floor. It had belonged to Ellen Terry, grandmother of my father's second wife. There is also the pastel peony drawing made by my father's mythical first wife, Iris; the bicycle he fell off on the ice once; the huge liver bird urn that our lodger, Professor Zibbert, received when he retired. My mother used to put black tulips in the urn. I found an inchworm in there once. I took it with me to see the Pope, it got stuck in the gap of my smocked dress and I squashed it trying to get it out. My mother thought I was crying because I was overcome by seeing the Pope. This reinforced her belief that I was a changeling, over secretive and psychic. The urn is empty now bar two bamboo sticks. I see the tea caddy that my sister brought back from Valencia and my father's velour wingback chair that still smells of cigars 15 years after he's given them up.

The Victorian Schoolhouse that my father now lives in is composed of years of remnants shoring up upon one another. It has rising damp and 'Jew's Ear' growing in it. It has four shaved corners to prevent children hurting themselves on the sharp red brick that provides a home for masonry bees. The sulphur yellow of the walls shows through from the 1960s, the Beryl blue of the 1950s beneath that. Darwin described the shadows of the glaciers he saw in Tierra del Fuego as Beryl blue: a reference to Werner's *Nomenclature of Colours,* the visual taxonomy of colours that he had on board the Beagle. Werner's *Nomenclature* was divided into a grid of animals, vegetables, and minerals with a colour that corresponded to each category: the same shade of blue that appeared on the beauty spot on the wing of a teal drake, the celandine flower, and the berries on the margaritaria tree matched that of mineral Beryl.

The inside reminds me of the catacombs of Paris, with their walls of compact skulls. There is just enough space for my father to walk through the newspapers that fill every room of the house. Like a badger's set, he has carved out compartments. One compartment houses his chair. It is on the dais of a textured rug, maybe a rag-rug, I can't work it out. I can't get close enough because the pouf is in another cell like compartment and I can't see easily around the corner. The geological strata of the newspapers that surrounds me must cover at least 30 years. The Vitruvian dimensions of this habitat are fitted to my father alone. I am shorter than he is and when I walk through the tunnels there is a gap above me, as if my head is in a coffin. 'Enough space for the skull not to make a sound during the service,' an undertaker had told me.

Figure 76

On April 8th, 1947, Artie Matthews, a local workman, discovered the body of the compulsive hoarder, Langley Collyer, just ten feet from where his brother, Homer died. Langley's partially rotted body was being eaten by rats. A suitcase and three huge bundles of newspapers covered him. Langley had been crawling through a homemade newspaper tunnel to bring food to his paralysed brother when one of his own booby traps fell and crushed him. Homer, blind and paralysed, starved to death several days later. The stench detected on the street had been emanating from Langley, the younger of the two men.

Figure 77

From the pouf I see a postcard of Versailles. I look at it while my father talks. When Versailles was built this ridiculously grand palace, with acres of looking glass, gold, and malachite had no water closet and King and servant alike often shat on the Pavonazzo marble stairs. Next to it is an engraving of Venice propped on a pile of squash racquets. Venice is a chimera, a city of over 200 15th century palaces, aching with glittering, cut glass chandeliers, floating on a milky lagoon that percolates with rotting vegetal matter. In a Venetian carnival, the fool is King for the day and the King is a fool. Literature has acknowledged the disquieting beauty of Venice: the liquorice slug that trickles down the forehead of Gustav von Aschenbach, dying as lust devours him amid the stench of cholera in *Death in Venice*; the red anorak of the longed-for daughter, and murderous dwarf in *Don't Look Now;* and Shakespeare's bloodthirsty Shylock. My father looks to see what I am looking at and says he has a house in Venice now. He talks in Italian now too, with a rococo rolling of his 'r's; a decorative trifle on the putrefying past he has constructed, submerged again now, a ghost in the narrow stone walls of the city. Thomas Mann was staying at the Grand Hotel des Bains on the Lido when he espied Baron Wladyslaw Moes, or so his wife tells interviewers in the 1970s, and he let his imagination consume him almost to destruction. It is within the atmosphere of this overwhelming and supernatural island shimmering in the ozone, above the lagoon at the Grand Hotel des Bains, that he writes of his longing for the boy in a sailor suit named Paris.

Before I leave, I look closer at the rug under the chair. It is the only item I don't recognise. I realise the rug is composed of hundreds of apple cores entwined and fluffy: a rat king of discarded fruit that has become a living breathing organism, a unique interior addition. 'I like your rug. Is it Axminster?' I ask as I leave, and shake my father's hand.

Figure 78

At school, whenever I fell over and skinned my knee in the car park or cut my chin on the concrete steps outside the woodwork room, other pupils thought I was crying because it hurt. I tried a few different things to cover up the wounds: calamine, talc, powdered mustard. The blood just absorbed Max Factor face powder again and again, and the wound came into focus as soon as you blotted it out. Poster paint mixed with PVA was good if you could keep totally still but cracked as soon as you moved. A group of people from the theatre came to school once and showed us pan stick, and that was good too, but one of the women saw me studying it intently and whipped it away. 'Want to cover your freckles, do you?' 'No' I said, mentally adding another thing to the list of things to feel neurotic about. My father had only just told me that medieval people thought redheads were born due to sex during menstruation.

*

It would happen on Sundays. My sister Ruth and I would have wrestled on the spare bed, she would be Big Daddy and I'd be some lacklustre opponent like Davey Boy Smith or Gentleman Chris Adams. We would pull the blanket straight afterwards like surgeons straightening the operation area up. I would look at the forbidden Reader's Digest Atlas in my father's study. *Wonders of the World* was my favourite page and showed close-up photographs of rocks and minerals. We would listen out for the Peugeot on the gravel and wait in the sitting room doing some stunt homework or pretend to read. Then my mother would come in and say whose turn it was first. We had to go in separately.

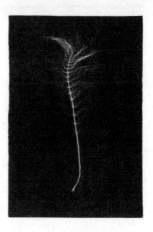

Figure 79

Years later I bought a copy of the same Atlas on eBay:

:-) Never done it before, but I've just been into PayPal and requested a payment of £13.50 which (apparently) they will request from you. Once you've paid it let me know (they may – I'm not sure) & I'll mark it as paid and post to you. I hope you get a lot of use from the book, it was my son's, he was killed in an accident 9½ years ago aged 24. :-(

Figure 80

My father would be sitting on the bed. Sometimes he'd say 'You're too early.' This was the worst thing because instead of being allowed to go, you had to wait while he took his sweaty squash tracksuit off and went upstairs in his ludicrously short towelling robe. Then he'd come down naked. My mother would bring him in some dandelion root coffee (she would dig the dandelions up from the lawn to make it). He'd make us sit at her once plush 1970s vanity unit. It had dressing room lights but only one of them worked now, and a unit for a shaver, but my father had a beard. I didn't see a man shave until I got the overnight train from Carlisle to the New Forest a few years later and a man in the carriage shaved with a big electric razor that looked like a bar of black soap.

My father would get the Swann Morton box (established, 1932) out of his bedside cupboard while we had to silently get down to our pants. Next, he'd put a new blade in the scalpel holder and starting from our head look for scabs. I presume it was the same for each of us. We never actually said. My sister still has Krakatoa as we used to call it on the top of her foot, a sort of tumulus left from my father's excavations. He'd wanted to be a doctor but left school at 13.

Figure 81

I was my father's only real blood daughter. My older sisters' real father, Francis, was the man that my father wanted to be: cultured, wealthy; with a First from Trinity College and a famous father, relations that were in *Burke's Peerage*, and a great uncle with a colour named after him, Lovett Green. Most importantly they were eminent Victorians. A Victorian man was my father's natural blueprint he felt. When we visited the Victoria and Albert Museum he related to the Victorian chairs, the wallpaper, the literature, and the moral codex. It was, he felt, the beginning of logic and the appreciation of its inherent value in all things. It was the beginning too of symbolism and the flourishing of forbidden love. Each Christmas my father borrowed the TV and VHS player from the children's home that he ran. There were three videos we could watch: *Tess* (of the d'Urbervilles) (1979), *The French Lieutenant's Woman* (1981) and my father on *The Pyramid Game* (1985) with Duncan Goodhew and Sally James, who he said was a thick, stupid woman with synthetic fluff for brains.

My father had a dream to go on *Mastermind* with Darwin as his specialist subject, or second choice Thomas Hardy. We were in the room with the borrowed television when we heard Magnus Magnusson announce that the contestant Robert Hughes, a retired policeman from London, was to do Darwin, and then John Moorhouse, a GP from Surrey, was to do Thomas Hardy. We all left the room gradually, knowing that a violent rage would ensue, not least because my father had always wanted to be a GP often illegally putting Dr. before his name. He also despised policeman, and said they were all cretins (his estranged brother Nigel was a detective, and this, he said was proof above all else that they took any idiot). My father thought that I was 'educationally subnormal' as I wrote his name in mirror writing, on his leg cast. He had broken his kneecap chasing one of the borstal boys over a brick wall.

Figure 82

A hot day in Liverpool meant that my dark skinned sisters would bake on top of the tarmac and felt roof of the garage. They were not allowed up there, but my father couldn't see them. They would make ice-lollies out of the vermouth that the Polish lodger had left in the larder and take a radio and diaries onto the roof along with a hairbrush and some Canadian ginger ale flavoured lip-gloss. If it was June, I would take the

Quality Street jar Ramona from our street gave me, in the hope I could lasso a swarm of bees with it.

> A swarm of bees in May
> Is worth a load of hay.
> A swarm of bees in June
> Is worth a silver spoon.
> A swarm of bees in July
> Is not worth a fly.

Esther would draw dresses and dress patterns, which she would cut out. Hannah would write secretly and so would Susannah. I would draw and paint and have plasticine. Esther would make us lunch out of Smash and Angel Delight and anything powdered that we could buy from the shop where Ramona worked. We were jealous of Ramona, as her father gave her so much freedom, and were shocked by our neighbour who said that Indian men were autocratic. One summer I picked some of the weeds that had crept through the felt on the roof. I pressed them and made a card for my botanist grandmother. I kept it for months, ready for her visit. My father had grapefruit for breakfast and my mother let me keep the pips and grow them in the airing cupboard under my sisters' knickers. I did the same with an avocado pip from my father's lunch. We weren't allowed avocados or grapefruits, as they were too expensive. We weren't allowed trout either and I was glad as its popped fizzy white eyes looked disgusting.

I was also given a black tulip bulb and any weeds, which were pretty like Scarlet Pimpernel, bindweed, vetch, and saxifrage.

'If we pushed him off a ladder he'd survive like Rasputin and then he'd be paralysed, and we'd have to look after him till he died.'
'You'd have to breastfeed him' said Ruth to Hannah, and Hannah said 'mmm' and nodded.

'You'd have to cut his toenails,' Hannah said to me and I thought of our father's long yellow toenails that looked like his father's nicotine stained fingernails.

'I tried digging holes in the ground so that he might fall down one' I said.

Esther rolled over onto her stomach and rested her head on her folded hands like a girl on TV.

'I heard that Prince Albert died of Saturnism' said Hannah, 'From the pipes at Osborne House'.

'I heard on the radio if you boil frozen peas and then you reheat them it can poison you. But he doesn't eat peas.'

'We need to get bread from the Roch Briand bakery, and then we can give him ergot poisoning'

'I don't think they still sell that bread though' said Esther.

'Grace of Monaco had some wires cut in her car. By Rosicrucian's. And they made her have sex with a hairbrush.'

Biscuit yawns and lets out a whimper. Her black rubber jaws wobble, she put a paw on her soggy baby shoe. Gravy Browning looks alert and we all turn to look, to see what she sees. 'She's just seen the ghost of Fuzzy Bear the Royal Turbot, that's all' says Ruth. Gravy Browning reverses the arch of her tired back onto Biscuit's blonde tummy and closes her furry eyelids. When we come back from holiday in Gairloch, Gravy Browning hears the burglar who is creeping up each storey of the house ahead of us. When he gets to the top, she follows him down the fire escape. She is hoping he has food. She has ESP of all sorts. Fuzzy Bear has her kittens in a box on the garage roof. They are born in a caul. I remember this years later watching the film *The Conversation*. Harry Caul wears an embryonic jelly mac, and the description he gives of slipping down into the bath and regaining consciousness greased all over in holy water, is an indication of his ability to resist drowning. Cauls were sold for high prices to sailors who would be immune from drowning if they wore it on them always, and so it became a medieval midwife's perk to steal one. One in a thousand are now born with a caul and most parents don't realise as the doctor or midwife usually punctures and bins the evidence. Liberace, King Zog, Freud, and Freud's Wolfman were all born with cauls.

'Ornithologists from Oxford have found a 2500 year-old bird's nest on a cliff in Greenland.' I say. Everyone ignores this. It took me ages to work out how to say the number.

Esther loved telling the story of Jane Maria Clouson: 'Murdered by the man who got her pregnant. She said his name before she died but the judge called it hearsay. Local people paid for her tomb, a kneeling girl on its own in the trees. She still appeared. Her face a waterfall of blood. Until they built over the alley where it happened.'

'What if they build over the garage?' Hannah said.

Figure 83

It never occurred to us to not turn the engine of the Peugeot off when my father shut himself in it with a hosepipe leading to the exhaust.

It was on one of these occasions that my father resurfaced from unconsciousness to perceive a weed growing through the garage roof. Our 'garden' had been revealed, as had the rope ladder to the roof and my sisters' strongbox with magazines and diaries in. My father cut the padlock off with an axe and read them aloud at dinner, scoffing particularly at descriptions of period pain and a joint crush on a boy, and how my sisters had saved up to buy his wellies from Oxfam because they had his name written inside, in marker pen. As we sat silently listening, I felt a pleasure and a red hot fear that we were sitting at the table where my sisters wrote the names of the boys they liked underneath and where we all made drawings, mine mostly of our pets. I was too young to be allowed crushes.

We weren't permitted on the roof anymore and Garston Docks, next door, put up barbed wire. My sister Esther started hiding her diary under the quilt of her doll's cot, along with a birthday card she got from her friend Miranda. It was a naked man and he looked nothing like my father. On the front it said, 'In case you haven't seen one of these in a while.' I kept my seeds and snail box inside my piano. Later when I got a stick insect from school he climbed up the green velvet curtains that Scarlet O' Hara would have easily turned into a dress and lived at the top, coming down only for privet.

As a punishment we were separated by my father. We sisters could not be so rotten on our own. We had chickpea tin and string 'telephones' that rarely worked. We tried bird call, ringing the servant's bells for nonexistent servants a certain number of times, and playing different songs on the record player. In the end, we all listened to the radio on the same channel in *solidarnosc*. My mother loathed this, called us the village of the damned children. I was blamed because of Mickey, my psychic Welsh grandmother.

Figure 84

I found a long eared bat electrocuted by a pylon and I sealed it in one of my mother's Swiss Air envelopes. Hoping it would mummify, I put it in the airing cupboard where it stank and oozed onto the back of my father's Viyella shirt in a perfect bat shape. He wore it at work until one of the children told him they could see his bat. I liked the feel of the central cord of gristle of a rat dusted by a fine down of velvet, like Johnny Town mouse in his fine gabardine mac. Like Samuel Whiskers in his three piece suit, these Victorian gents were plopped into my wheelbarrow along with black tulip petals, rolled up earwigs, and daddy long-legs. Once when she was telling me off my mother dropped a Georgian silver spoon into the food disposal unit. This rendered the whole set a third of its original value and wrecked the grinding knives. In the future, the house details declared: 'waste disposal unit (defunct).'

Figure 85

This morning, while sweeping the crumbs off the breakfast table Margaret, the cook, told Anna that the prayer *Abide With Me* had been set to music. Anna thinks of telling John, but it is hardly worth writing about such trivia in a letter. She imagines him telling the other men about his wife's letters bringing news of a hymnal set to music. It smells of honey and carpet beating day in the room. The parquet had been recently polished with beeswax from the Norbert's hives. They had got aggressive and needed a new queen. Rebecca, the maid, had been stung twice on her arm, but said it improved the arthritis in her wrist so she could not complain, despite it looking like a Christmas ham. There are other smells in there too, of the morning kedgeree and of an ox tongue, sitting in hot salted water in the kitchen. Anna lifts the jasper vase up and it leaves a ring on the teapoy. She knew Margaret would be cross. She blots it with a handkerchief, bringing out two from her sleeve by mistake. One lands on the floor. She pulls a maidenhair fern frond from the vase and places it on the table.

Walking over to her father's desk, Anna sees the green paper at the window cast a ghoulish shadow on the dog's pale ears. She finds the knife in her father's drawer, rolled up in grey suede with his pencil holder and an ivory letter opener. The chesty sound of a wood pigeon echoes down the chimney and makes her heartbeat louder. She pushes her hand into the darker parts of the desk and sees it is the unfinished scorched carpet moth specimen lying unpinned on a cotton cushion, a sort of open coffin. The flat back model of a shepherd and his wife fall face forward onto her father's blotting pad. She picks the thick blotting paper up and thinks of the queen's black blotting paper. Her father told her about that. 'What does the queen eat for breakfast?' she used to ask. 'Maybe a pineapple?' he would say, and she would squeal.

Figure 86

Anna is hot and frustrated; she doesn't know where anything is. She takes her thick bombazine matinee off and slings it on the nursery chair. She peels the mousseline off the blueprints she has left in a pile on the piano. She sees the light zephyr fabric has been eaten by moths exposing the prints to the sun again. She looks down at the cat. As it yawns it turns its head inside out like an umbrella in the wind. The labels, too, are written on very fine paper like rice paper. But rice paper will not come to England for another 20 years, so it is another man's recent invention that she uses: glass paper, created by the engraver M. Quenedy in 15 Rue des Petites Champs, Paris, in the 1820s.

Figures 87 & 88

Women couldn't be surgeons and a knife wasn't meant
for her hands. Anna takes off her bracelet and her ring
and rolls the watered silk sleeves beyond her elbows.
The billiard table has a soft surface and she knows that
Darwin used his for dissection. The low gas lights are
buzzing, and she goes to turn them off. She pulls the
merveilleux curtains back and dust rises in the daylight.
A bluebottle crashes and buzzes at the window and
Margot jumps and clatters her claws on the
windowpane. Stretching like a dancing bear in Berlin,
she shows her eight nipples to the light and her still
pregnant looking belly swings on the back of the damask
sofa. Grimacing, she closes one eye to chew the fly.

Figure 89

Anna's coral bracelet clinks on the glass that she uses to press her specimens, ready for printing. She pushes it up her arm, past the burn she got from the hissing willow log that lurched out of the grate close to Sammy's tail. She is beginning to get white freckles now that look like the specks of fat in meat sausage. She picks the poppy up with the dry pads of the forefingers of her left hand. She reverts to these when she is in private. She has more confidence in her left side. She wiggles her finger and thumb tips into the chalk cube, wipes them on her skirt, leaving a white streak of the crumbled shells that Kent is made of. Her mother's seed pearl ring will be worn by a stranger, Erica Lucy Jacobs, because Anna doesn't have any children. Now though, she submerges it in the water of the well so many times she feels it revert to its former oceanic home.

Figure 90

She lets the cat out through the glass door. The poppy gangles and the head looks like a Madame de Pompadour coiffure and the stalk looks long and unhealthy. Anna cuts the stalk and cuts the leaf. She sees a marigold leaf and she cuts and sutures it onto the poppy stalk. The sun develops her mistakes, a patch of cyanotype dye that is blue turns into a black bruise on the back of the rug by the sofa. Many years later this oval stain will become a doll's house pond for a child called Eliza Morten, as she plays on the floor in this same room. A gang of long tailed tits arrive in the willow tree and began to shout at the cat. The cat waits at the door, with her body low and her ears pulled back, wailing.

Figures 91 & 92

'Algae,' it says in Anna Atkins' near complete album in the British Library, 'has an unknown etymology. It may come from *alliga*, meaning binding and intertwining.' Anna, following Linnaeus' binomial nomenclature, which presents plants as belonging to various branches of a family tree, with a 'mother'(genus) and a 'father' (family) arranges her algae into groups of siblings.

Figure 93

List of Illustrations

20. Whistle and I'll Come to You (film still), dir. Jonathan Miller, 1968.

21. Blue Hose, a Close-up From 'A Burial at Ornans,' Courbet, 1849-50, Annabel Dover, 2014.

22. Tony Corke's Drawer, Annabel Dover, 2013.

23. Rebecca (film still), dir. Alfred Hitchcock, 1940.

24. Rebecca (film still), dir. Alfred Hitchcock, 1940.

25. Rebecca (film still), dir. Alfred Hitchcock, 1940.

26. Herbarium of Fuci, 1862, Annabel Dover, 2020.

27. Ectoplasm Photograph, c.1900.

28. Unknown Girl, Annabel Dover, 2010.

29. Still life With Joe Orton & Kenneth Halliwell's flat, 1960-1967, Annabel Dover, 2020.

30. Full Moon, Lewis Morris Rutherfurd, 1871, reproduced with permission of The Metropolitan Museum of Art.

31. Pair of Eyes, 5th Century B.C. or later, Greek, reproduced with permission of The Metropolitan Museum of Art.

32. Venice I, Annabel Dover, 2013.

33. Venice II, Annabel Dover, 2013.

34. Venice III, Annabel Dover, 2013.

35. Orpheus, Annabel Dover, 2010.

36. Lucca, Annabel Dover, 1999.

37. Inscribed First Copy of 'Alice's Adventures Underground' Given to Alice Liddell by Charles Dodgson, 1886, Annabel Dover, 2020.

38. The Prettiest Doll in the World, Lewis Carroll, 1870, reproduced with permission of The Metropolitan Museum of Art.

39. Grey Gardens (film still), dir. Albert Maysles, 1975.

40. Funerary Mask, 250-300 BC, Egypt, reproduced with permission of The Metropolitan Museum of Art.

41. Dummy Head Used by Prisoner to Escape Alcatraz in 1962, Annabel Dover, 2020.

42. Still Life With Hermine Moos' Doll of Oskar Kokoschka's Wife, 1919, Annabel Dover, 2015.

43. Carnegie, Justine Moss, 2012.

44. Patrick Syme's 'Werner's Nomenclature of Colours', 1821, Annabel Dover, 2001.

45. Cyanometer, Horace-Bénédict de Saussure, 1760, reproduced with permission of Bibliothèque de Genève, Arch. de Saussure 66/7.

46. January 3rd, Jason Manning, 2015.

71. *Gloves*, Alexandrine, c.1867, reproduced with permission of The Metropolitan Museum of Art.

72. *Refugee hostel: Rima's Objects*, Annabel Dover, 2017.

73. *Daddy's Valentine*, Annabel Dover, 2001.

74. *Sanitary Towel Disposal Bag*, Annabel Dover, 1998.

75. *Fused Sewing Needles*, 1945, reproduced with permission of Hiroshima Peace Memorial Museum.

76. *Crown Street*, Annabel Dover, 2006.

77. *Greenfinch Nest With Confetti, 1865*, Annabel Dover, 2009.

78. *May pole dance,* 1917, reproduced with permission of University of Wisconsin Collection.

79. *Horsetail From My Father's Garden*, Annabel Dover, 2003.

80. *Monkeys*, Annabel Dover, 2001.

81. *Picnic at Hanging Rock* (film still), dir. Peter Weir, 1975.

82. *Fused Cups*, Yukio Nakata, 1945, reproduced with permission of Hiroshima Peace Memorial Museum.

83. *Sugar Bowl With the Words: 'East India sugar not made by slaves. By six families using East India, instead of West India sugar, one slave less is required.'* 1825, © Museum of London.

84. *Picnic at Hanging Rock* (film still), dir. Peter Weir, 1975.

85. *Himanthalia lorea*, Anna Atkins, c.1853, reproduced with permission of The Metropolitan Museum of Art.

86. *Picnic at Hanging Rock* (film still), dir. Peter Weir, 1975.

87. *Waster of 34 Dishes Fused Together*, 1650-1670, reproduced with permission of the Victoria and Albert Museum, London.

88. *Polka Dot Goyotaku Plaice*, Mimei Thompson, 2013.

89. *Refugee Hostel: Abeer's My Little Pony*, Annabel Dover, 2017.

90. *Lady Isabella Hertford's Wallpaper at Temple Newsam, 1827*, Annabel Dover, 2015.

91. *Botanical Study*, Mary Delany, c.1772-82, reproduced with permission of The Metropolitan Museum of Art.

92. *Sankta Lucia*, Annabel Dover, 2001.

93. *Southern Sealion at London Zoo*, Wolf Suschitzky, 1955, reproduced with permission of Julia Donat.

Photographs introducing chapters one and two are: *Papaver Orientale*, Anna Atkins, c.1853, reproduced with permission of the Victoria and Albert Museum, London, and *Kalymenia dubyi*, Anna Atkins, 1853, reproduced with permission of The Metropolitan Museum of Art.

About the Author

Annabel Dover was born in Liverpool and studied Fine Art at Newcastle University, Central Saint Martins, and Wimbledon College of Art. Known for using a variety of media including photography, her art practice explores the role that objects play in social relationships. A set of Dover's cyanotypes were recently acquired by The Imperial War Museum, and also feature in the art historian Carol Mavor's *Blue Mythologies*. *Florilegia* is her first book.

Florilegia is the second book in MOIST's first season.
The other titles in 'A Trilogy of Alienation' are:

Equilibrium by Tonino Guerra
My Other Spruce and Maple Self by Susan Finlay